P45

First Edition

PRANGMERE MESS

PRANGMERE MESS

And Other Tales

by

ANTHONY ARMSTRONG

METHUEN & CO., LTD., LONDON
36 *Essex Street, Strand,* W.C.2

FOR
MICHAEL SHEPLEY
Because he likes it

First published in 1945

THIS BOOK IS PRODUCED IN
COMPLETE CONFORMITY WITH THE
AUTHORIZED ECONOMY STANDARD

PRINTED IN GREAT BRITAIN

CONTENTS

All the articles in this volume have appeared in *Punch*, to the Proprietors of which journal the Author wishes to express his gratitude for permission to reprint.

PART I

COMMITTEE MEETING REPORTS FROM THE R.A.F. MESS, PRANGMERE

FLIES

IN the R.A.F. Mess, Prangmere, a self-appointed committee went into session on Sunday night to discuss a topic of outstanding interest to the whole of the Royal Air Force. The question before the meeting was, in short, just how *does* a fly land on the ceiling.

Pilot-Officer Prune, opening the proceedings, said he was of the opinion the fly cruised along at the correct height below the ceiling and then did a half-loop, landing upwards at the top of the loop.

Squadron-Leader Undercart said that was all very well, but how did the fly judge his distance, so as to avoid nose-diving into the ceiling a quarter way through the loop? Presumably he wasn't fitted with an altimeter that worked inversely from the ceiling downwards instead of from the ground up. He personally took a poor view of Prune's theory.

Pilot-Officer Stall said he didn't get that half-loop idea either, though for exactly the opposite reason. Surely, as soon as the fly lost flying speed sufficiently to effect a good three-pointer ceiling landing, he would stall in an upside-down position, go into an inverted nose-dive, and have to pull out of it by completing the loop and, so to speak, going round again. The same thing would probably happen several times before he hit it off at last, which would mean that the majority of flies—especially the inexperienced ones who had only just joined the squadron from their O.T.U.—would be making a series of vertical circuits before getting a "bump," a thing he had never seen yet—and please God never would! He here stopped for lack of breath.

Flight-Lieutenant Lyne-Shute said let them fight it out between themselves: he personally was ordering a beer.

Pilot-Officer Nosedyve said that any sort of landing made at the top of a loop meant that the fly landed facing in the opposite way to his direction of flight, which must be very confusing to the ceiling-staff, though very useful if the fly found he was overshooting on coming in.

Flying-Officer Flaps said he too thought the loop theory was just sheer bull. The normal act of landing was really stalling, and you couldn't stall upwards! It'd be much the same sort of thing as having your aircraft drop up to stratosphere just as you were going to touch down—like that, see! What *he* thought the fly really did was to come in close up—like *that*!—do a half slow-roll—like *that*!—and there he was, going gently along still in the direction of flight—like THAT! Sorry!

Flight-Lieutenant Lyne-Shute said that if Flying-Officer Flaps had been in the R.F.C. in 1915 he'd have learnt to keep his hands under control: now he'd have to order more beer.

Pilot-Officer Rudder said perhaps the tougher fighter flies, with many hours' operational flying behind them, had some wizard landing dodge of their own—especially with those sticky feet, which had the most powerful brakes beat to a frazzle. He suggested that they might zoom right up to the ceiling, suddenly put a leg up and come up, all standing.

Pilot-Officer Nosedyve said the strain on the fly's undercarriage if he did that must be terrific: it would certainly be against fly flying regulations.

Flight-Lieutenant Lyne-Shute said the very idea made him feel faint and he was ordering some beer.

Squadron-Leader Undercart said a fly didn't have one undercarriage only: he had six.

Pilot-Officer Stall said, surely eight.

Squadron-Leader Undercart said, nuts, six.

Flying-Officer Talespin said it was common knowledge that the house-fly, or *Musca domestica*, possessed . . . His speech was interrupted by the attempts of Pilot-Officer Stall and Squadron-Leader Undercart each trying to try to bring down a fly and prove the other wrong. No victory, however, could be confirmed, though several combats took place, in one of which Squadron-Leader Undercart claimed a "probable," the fly attacked being last seen, he stated, heading for home with black smoke coming from its port wing.

Flight-Lieutenant Lyne-Shute said that if they'd *quite* finished upsetting his beer, he'd order some . . .

Flying-Officer Talespin, interrupting, said how about the fly turning on its back and flying upside down when nearing the ceiling level, if they saw what he meant.

Flying-Officer Flaps said something rude about upside down, Flying-Officer Talespin, what he meant, and flies in general.

Flying-Officer Talespin disagreed. . . .

Wing-Commander Blower said, now, boys, chuck it and, anyway, if one wanted to get the real gen on the fly-landing business they ought to get up close to the landing ground and watch.

There was then another lull in the discussion, while Squadron-Leader Undercart, two Flying-Officers and three Pilot-Officers formed a pyramid to enable Pilot-Officer Prune at the top to examine the flying ground situation and report. Wing-Commander Blower turned on the cornice lights to give the flies a proper flare path, and said they should be warned that an electric-light-pendant barrage was flying in the centre of the ceiling. He was still looking round for a torch as an angle-of-glide indicator when Squadron-Leader Undercart, who was the base of the pyramid, suddenly got tired. The object of the exercise was thus not achieved.

Flight-Lieutenant Lyne-Shute asked heatedly which of them it was that had upset his beer this time: now he'd have to order some more.

Group-Captain Boost, taking part in the discussion for the first time, said no one was ordering more beer, it was late enough as it was: if they felt so keen about the thing, let them write to the Brains Trust: meanwhile Lyne-Shute was to take off for his quarters at once, to be followed by the others at three seconds' intervals, or else . . .

Thereupon the meeting broke up and the Mess emptied in half a minute.

The flies continued to alight on the ceiling in their own inscrutable fashion.

WASPS

THE following night, Monday, the R.A.F. Mess, Prangmere, held another Committee meeting. The proceedings were opened by Group-Captain Boost, who said for heaven's sake to keep off flies to-night, things were . . . *would* Pilot-Officer Prune kindly stop mumbling to Flying-Officer Talespin in that corner: if he had anything to say, for God's sake speak up and let 'em all hear.

Blushing deeply, Pilot-Officer Prune said, sorry, sir, he was just saying, sir, that it was *his* half-loop theory, sir, that had gained most favour, sir, and that he was just telling Talespin, who had, both at the time and now, disagreed, to put a sock in it, sir.

Group-Captain Boost accepted the explanation.

Flying-Officer Talespin, resuming with heat, gave it as his considered opinion that Prune was a clot.

Flight-Lieutenant Lyne-Shute, speaking to a waiter, gave it as his considered opinion that he wanted some beer.

Flying-Officer Talespin amended his previous statement to include twirp, adding that if Prune was so clever let him answer *this* one, and that, yes, he thought he'd join Flight-Lieutenant Lyne-Shute in a light ale.

Pilot-Officer Prune, in conjunction with Pilot-Officers Nosedyve and Stall, asked what one.

Flying-Officer Talespin said this one he was going to ask now, couldn't a chap pause a second in conversation to order a drink without a horde of lower forms of life leaping down his throat? . . .

Wing-Commander Blower said now boys, chuck it, mind the furniture, let's hear the problem, anyway.

Flying-Officer Talespin said if you had a largish box with a wasp in it, said wasp just taxy-ing about the floor of the box, did the box weigh the same when the wasp took off and became air-borne?

Wing-Commander Blower, Flying-Officer Flaps and Pilot-Officer Rudder, speaking together, said of course it did: while simultaneously Squadron-Leader Undercart and Pilot-Officer Stall said of course it didn't. Flight-Lieutenant Lyne-Shute said here's how and Flying-Officer Talespin said mud in his (Lyne-Shute's) eye.

There was a pause. Group-Captain Boost then said well, what's the answer?

Flying-Officer Talespin, speaking with embarrassed respect, said he didn't know, it was a moot point.

Group-Captain Boost said very moot and laughed heartily. Pilot-Officer Rudder at once also laughed heartily and somewhat fulsomely.

Squadron-Leader Undercart said that once in the air the wasp, like an aircraft, ceased to press on the ground or floor of the box: therefore there was that much less pressure and so weight.

Wing-Commander Blower said so what? Something was keeping the wasp up—he presumed, of course, it was circling the landing-ground—and that was the air-pressure from underneath: this must be transmitted downwards as well and be distributed over the floor of the box equivalent to the weight of a wasp.

Flying-Officer Flaps wondered how much a wasp weighed, anyway, and was ignored.

Flight-Lieutenant Lyne-Shute said the thought of the poor wasp circling made him quite dizzy and he needed some beer to restore him. Pilot-Officer Nosedyve said that was an idea—him too.

Pilot-Officer Rudder said he agreed with the Wing-Commander, there was a box with a wasp and some air, no not hot air, don't interrupt, which must weigh the same whether the wasp was stoogeing around the 'drome or definitely grounded at Dispersal.

Rather shamefacedly, Flying-Officer Talespin said he should have mentioned at the start that the box had holes in it, so that the air-pressure theory probably didn't work.

Flying-Officer Flaps said how big were the holes?

Flying-Officer Talespin said it didn't matter, they let the air out.

Flying-Officer Flaps said it did matter, they might let the wasp out. It'd get tired of doing circuits and bumps, and push off on a sortie over a jam-pot or something.

Flight-Lieutenant Lyne-Shute said this thing was getting him down, he needed a little beer to pull him through.

Pilot-Officer Stall said if there were holes, the box *must* weigh less when the wasp took off. Pilot-Officer Prune said then where *was* the weight of the wasp, you couldn't have weightless wasps flying round any more than a weightless Spitfire. Squadron-Leader Undercart said bitterly a weightless Spitfire might be pretty useful for some people, particularly anyone who had damaged an undercarriage yesterday through a bad landing. Pilot-Officer Prune here picked up a magazine and took no further part in the discussion.

Wing-Commander Blower said, boys, let's be practical: fetch me a box and a wasp and the Mess kitchen scales.

A search-party was mustered, and there was then a lull in the discussion till Pilot-Officer Nosedyve, speaking on behalf of the search-party, reported a box as present and correct, would this wasp do which had just force-landed on the window-sill, and a waiter was bringing the scales.

Flight-Lieutenant Lyne-Shute said if the waiter was coming anyway, he might bring another beer while he was about it, in 1915 he'd have done it automatically.

The Committee inspected the wasp, while Flying-Officer Flaps held it up by one aileron, and reported it highly somnolent. Pilot-Officer Prune said perhaps it was a night-fighter wasp which slept all day. Squadron-Leader Under-cart said, don't talk so loud, you'll wake it. He unfortunately spoke too late. The wasp woke up, took off, and flew by Standard Beam Approach up Pilot-Officer Prune's sleeve. Here its rear-gunner put in a three-second burst which made Prune collide with the waiter carrying the scales, and the meeting adjourned in confusion, the last recorded minute being an inquiry by Flight-Lieutenant Lyne-Shute as to who was responsible for upsetting his beer.

PARROTS

I

THE R.A.F. Mess, Prangmere, went into committee on Tuesday night on the subject of parrots, Flying-Officer Flaps having that morning been unexpectedly presented with a parrot by a grateful sailor.

The proceedings were opened by Flying-Officer Flaps himself, who took a poor view of the presentation and inquired why for God's sake a parrot. Pilot-Officer Prune said that it was in the best tradition of the sea, sailors always had parrots. Flying-Officer Flaps said he wasn't worrying about sailors *having* parrots, he was worrying about sailors *giving away* parrots. Just because a fellow happened to be stoogeing around the North Sea and see some darn sailor on a raft didn't mean that he (the sailor) had subsequently to thrust hundreds of parrots upon him (Flaps), damn him (the sailor). Squadron-Leader Undercart agreed, why not something in which the whole Mess could share, say rum, that also was in the best tradition of the sea? Pilot-Officer Stall said who'd got *hundreds* of parrots? Flying-Officer Flaps said tersely, well, one then, anyway, it climbed about the cage so quick it looked like a whole operational squadron of parrots, if not a complete offensive sweep.

Flight-Lieutenant Lyne-Shute said Flying-Officer Flaps was evidently seeing things, too much beer he shouldn't wonder, talking of rum, would anyone join him in a stoup of ale. Pilot-Officer Nosedyve at once said wizard idea, and Pilot-Officer Prune concurred. Flight-Lieutenant Lyne-Shute thereupon called a waiter into committee and said three beers.

Pilot-Officer Prune said Flying-Officer Flaps didn't seem to be looking at this parrot in the right way, it was a gift. Flying-Officer Flaps said that was all very well, but the gift had bitten him twice. Pilot-Officer Prune said then Flying-Officer Flaps didn't seem to be *handling* this parrot in the right way. Flying-Officer Flaps said tchah. Flight-Lieutenant Lyne-Shute said, there was how: and Pilot-Officers Nosedyve and Prune said, there was looking at him, old man.

Appealing to the meeting, Flying-Officer Flaps inquired what could he do with a parrot anyway. A number of answers were received, none helpful and one (Flying-Officer Talespin) physiologically impracticable. Flying-Officer Flaps replied in general terms, adding a rider to the effect that

Flying-Officer Talespin thought himself ruddy funny, didn't he? Pilot-Officer Stall said, why didn't Flying-Officer Flaps cross his parrot with a carrier pigeon so that the Air Force could have pigeons capable of taking verbal messages, and Pilot-Officer Rudder said har, har, har, why, he baled out of his cradle when he first heard that one. Pilot-Officer Airscrew said, obviously then he hadn't remembered to pull his ripcord and so had landed on his head, which would account for his present low I.Q.

Pilot-Officer Rudder took considerable exception to this statement. Wing-Commander Blower said, now boys, chuck it, mind the furniture, and Flight-Lieutenant Lyne-Shute said, more important, mind his beer, the pair of them almost upset it, only luckily his can was just empty—why thanks, Prune, old man, he didn't mind if he did.

Flying-Officer Talespin said, referring back to this parrot, and Group-Captain Boost, putting down his paper and interrupting, said, speaking of parrots, could this parrot talk well? Flying-Officer Flaps said it knew several seafaring words, and probably . . . Group-Captain Boost said because if it could, he suggested that Flying-Officer Flaps should choose a mate for it from among . . . Flying-Officer Flaps said the parrot hadn't yet been properly overhauled by a competent mechanic and so he was still uncertain what operational type it . . . Group-Captain Boost, continuing a little tersely, said a mate for it from among the carrier pigeons so that the progeny could take verbal messages, eh? Pilot-Officer Rudder said, ha, ha, ha, da-amn good, sir, ha, ha, and asked Pilot-Officer Stall what he was looking at him like that for. Pilot-Officer Stall answered briefly and loudly, though without employing any actual words. Pilot-Officer Rudder resented the comment and Wing-Commander Blower said how many times was he to tell them to chuck that.

Flying-Officer Flaps said this wasn't getting him anywhere with his parrot, had anyone any suggestions, and Flying-

Officer Talespin could keep his trap shut this time. Squadron Leader Undercart said he knew a grand story about a parrot, but on second thoughts perhaps he'd better not tell it. Pilot-Officers Prune, Nosedyve and Stall said, oh, sir, come on, sir, and Squadron-Leader Undercart said, well, it seemed there was once a fellow whose aunt had a . . . (*The following part of the report has been deleted by order of the Station Commander, Group-Captain Boost, D.F.C., A.F.C., R.A.F.*) Pilot-Officer Nosedyve said he also had an aunt who also had a wizard parrot, one that could say practically anything, the most cracking phrases, absolutely wizard it was. Flight-Lieutenant Lyne-Shute said meditatively, could it ask anyone to have a drink. Pilot-Officer Nosedyve said that probably it—oh, was it his turn. Flight-Lieutenant Lyne-Shute indicated that the answer was in the affirmative and that his was the same.

Pilot-Officer Stall said had anyone heard the story—Pilot-Officer Rudder excepted, who, of course, had jettisonned his comforter and baled out of his pram when he first heard it—about the man who bid up to an enormous price at an auction for a parrot and when he went up to pay, asked if it could talk, and was told why, of course, guv'nor, it had been bidding against him for half an hour. Pilot-Officer Rudder said, answering Stall's question, no he hadn't heard the story, go on, what was it? Pilot-Officer Stall said shortly, that was it. Pilot-Officer Rudder said Oh. Pilot-Officer Stall said, what did he mean, Oh. Wing-Commander Blower said, if you two boys don't stop . . .

Group-Captain Boost said suddenly, he'd never heard so much natter in his life *about* a parrot without *seeing* a parrot. Let the damn parrot be present to-morrow night, and if it were fully operational verbally and its R/T was good, so much the better, at least it might have something intelligent to say, which would be a change, meanwhile it was time for bed.

PARROTS

II

TUESDAY'S committee meeting held in the R.A.F. Mess, Prangmere—subject under discussion, parrots —which was adjourned pending the attendance of Flying-Officer Flaps' parrot in person, was resumed the following night, Wednesday.

On resumption, the bird in its cage was introduced to Group-Captain Boost, who inquired, Well, pretty Poll, how was a Polly, then? The parrot said nuts, and Flying-Officer Flaps hastily said it didn't really mean it like that, sir, it was merely asking for its staple food, much as Flight-Lieutenant Lyne-Shute might answer a similar query by stating that his was a beer. Flight-Lieutenant Lyne-Shute said, well, now, that was very kind of Flying-Officer Flaps, he hadn't actually heard his query, but in point of fact his *was* a beer. Flying-Officer Flaps referred back briefly to the parrot's last remark, and associated himself with the sentiment expressed. Flight-Lieutenant Lyne-Shute said if he felt like that about it, it could be on him (Lyne-Shute) then, waiter, two beers.

The parrot then, addressing Group-Captain Boost and Squadron-Leader Undercart, said, pretty Poll, scratch a poll, Polly, and put its crest up against the cage. Group-Captain Boost quickly said him (Undercart) first, and Squadron-Leader Undercart said after him (Boost), sir. Both then simultaneously said to Flying-Officer Flaps it was *his* parrot, to go on and scratch its damn dome for it, what was he waiting for? Flying-Officer Flaps said he'd been bitten twice already and only once bit was twice shy. Squadron-Leader Undercart said ah, that would be just its play, and Group-Captain Boost said hurry up, the bird was getting restless.

Flying-Officer Flaps reluctantly complied and then said

that made him six times shy, who'd got some plaster. Flight-Lieutenant Lyne-Shute said beer was best, cheeroh, old man.

Pilot-Officer Stall said the parrot was looking browned off, what about opening the hangar doors and letting it go out on ops? Pilot-Officer Rudder said lousy idea, they'd lose it: Flying-Officer Flaps said that was ruddy-well O.K. by him: Group-Captain Boost said go on, let them see what the bird's performance in flight was like, and Pilot-Officer Rudder said dashed good idea, sir. The parrot pointed out that it was to be Queen of the May, Mother, it was to be Queen of the May.

The hangar doors were opened and the parrot taxy-ed out on to the table. Pilot-Officer Nosedyve said look at it balancing first on one wheel of the undercart and then on the other, wasn't it wizard, he'd love to do that. Wing-Commander Blower said just let him (Blower) catch him (Nosedyve) trying it anywhere on the airfield and he (Nosedyve) would be torn off an imperial strip.

Group-Captain Boost said what was the parrot waiting for? Pilot-Officer Prune said perhaps the met. report wasn't favourable, certainly there was nine-tenths cloud in the Mess, mostly Flight-Lieutenant Lyne-Shute's pipe. The parrot said Cocky-cocky-cocky some eighteen times, and Flying-Officer Talespin suggested it was calling up Flying Control and wanted a green on the Aldis lamp.

Group-Captain Boost said shoo, and the parrot abruptly took off and gained height rapidly. Pilot-Officer Nosedyve said wizard, Wing-Commander Blower said now it was in flight one could see that it was an up-to-date operational type, and Squadron-Leader Undercart said yes, he would describe it as a grey mid-wing monoplane with retractable under-carriage, heavily armoured front turret and high yellow astrodome.

The parrot started a series of square searches, and Pilot-Officer Prune said it was looking for "intruders." Flight-

Lieutenant Lyne-Shute said he hoped it wasn't looking for ground targets, and rapidly finished his beer.

Calling up ground control, the parrot asked what was to be done with a drunken sailor. Pilot-Officer Prune told it. The parrot said chuckle-chawkaloo. Group-Captain Boost said what did it say, and Pilot-Officer Stall said he thought it had switched over to the intercom. and was telling the crew about Pilot-Officer Prune.

At this point the parrot sighted the Mess cat on the hearthrug and carried out a series of determined attacks from the red and green quarters alternately. The cat was badly panicked at first, but during the last attack put up a burst of flak with the right paw that severely damaged the parrot's rear turret. Several pieces of grey tail plane fell off and the parrot broke off the combat, steering a course straight out of the door with clouds of blue language pouring from it.

Flying-Officer Flaps said thank God for that, Flight-Lieutenant Lyne-Shute said it was his (Flaps') turn now and his (Lyne-Shute's) was another beer.

The committee then adjourned.

PARROTS

III

ON Thursday night the R.A.F. Mess, Prangmere, went very suddenly into Committee, owing to the unexpected return of Flying-Officer Flaps' parrot, which made a silent glide approach through the window and began to circle the aerodrome prior apparently to coming in to land.

Pilot-Officer Stall said blow him down, if it wasn't that damn parrot again. Flying-Officer Flaps said hell's bells, and he had been hoping it had force-landed somewhere out in the wilds and broken its ruddy neck. Pilot-Officer Prune said parrots didn't break their necks when they force-landed. Flying-Officer Flaps said they would, if they forgot to select their undercarriage down, they'd belly-land, tilt up on their nose and . . . Pilot-Officer Prune said parrots never broke their necks at any time, they hadn't that sort of air-frame, they could only get them wrung. Flying-Officer Flaps took a poor view of Pilot-Officer Prune's theory, referring to it as complete bull.

The parrot said cronklechawkleookerchonk, or words to that effect, and began to hover above the recumbent form of Flight-Lieutenant Lyne-Shute having a zizz on the settee after a long afternoon in the Ops. Room. Pilot-Officer Stall said what did it say, and Flying-Officer Talespin said its R/T didn't seem to be very good, but he thought it was asking what was its turn to land, please. Squadron-Leader Undercart said good Lord, it's mistaken Flight-Lieutenant Lyne-Shute's stomach for the flare-path, here, Lyne-Shute! . . . Wing-Commander Blower hastily said not to tell him, for Heaven's sake, not to tell him, give the bird a green on the Aldis lamp and see what happened. Pilot-Officer Rudder said cracking fine idea, sir, and Pilot-Officer Nosedyve said a-absolutely wizard.

The parrot made an engine-assisted approach, held off nicely at three inches, and made a perfect three-pointer landing without overshooting the boundary of Flight-Lieutenant Lyne-Shute's tunic.

Flight-Lieutenant Lyne-Shute said abruptly eeeeayeo-OW. The parrot said what a night, what a night, took off hastily and went round again. Flight-Lieutenant Lyne-Shute asked what the suffering sam was that. Flying-Officer Talespin said what was his trouble. Flight-Lieutenant Lyne-Shute thanked him and said his was a beer, and as he (Talespin) was nearest the bell . . .

The parrot set a course for the far end of the mess, did a

snappy Immelmann just above the radio and made good a reciprocal track to the fireplace end, where Group-Captain Boost was reading the paper.

Pilot-Officer Rudder said oh, sir, look out, sir, and covered his eyes. The parrot just banked round Group-Captain Boost's head in time, using a lot of rudder, and, calling up Flying Control, requested them to roll out the barrel.

Group-Captain Boost said what was that, was it that infernal parrot again, shoot it down someone and put it back in its hangar, it looked as though it were going to dive-bomb him any minute. Squadron-Leader Undercart said he thought it was only making dummy runs. Flight-Lieutenant Lyne-Shute said he for one was taking no chances, down the hatch, Talespin, old man, but let's have the other half.

The parrot pointed out that in its opinion there'd be no promotion this side of the ocean, so cheer up, its lads . . . Squadron-Leader Undercart here winged it with a matchbox and its R/T luckily packed up. Pilot-Officers Stall and Rudder next came into action with heavy flak—magazines and books from the mess table—and for some while the barrage was intense. The parrot took skilful avoiding action throughout and Pilot-Officer Nosedyve said it would be wizard on an operational sortie. Wing-Commander Blower said that he'd like to see it over Berlin. Group-Captain Boost said personally he intended to see it in its cage or know the reason why, get cracking. Flight-Lieutenant Lyne-Shute said whoever threw that Bradshaw would have to buy him another beer.

At this point the parrot came down low and began hedge-hopping the chairs. A lucky burst from a rolled up *Express* (Flying-Officer Talespin) caused it to crash-land in an arm-chair. Squadron-Leader Undercart, operating the heaviest flak yet seen, a cushion, said got it, dammit, he hadn't, yes,

B

by Jove, he had, it was underneath, pull it out, someone.

Four Pilot-Officers and one Flying-Officer pointed out it was Flying-Officer Flaps' parrot. Flying-Officer Flaps said the hell with that, its front gunner was still in action and he'd been bitten three times already, let it have a taste of someone else.

Group-Captain Boost said he'd give Flying-Officer Flaps just five minutes, what about it?

Flying-Officer Flaps thereupon returned the bird to its hangar with a skilful grip on the top of the fuselage. The parrot said a large number of things which would have been quite unrepeatable—except that Flying-Officer Flaps, on releasing it, became a casualty for the fourth time and repeated most of them.

Flight-Lieutenant Lyne-Shute said in the old days in the R.F.C. people never threw Bradshaws, who was it, and the Committee meeting was then terminated.

BATS

THE subject under discussion at the committee meeting held on Friday night in the R.A.F. Mess, Prangmere, was bats. A representative of the subject under discussion was present, arriving through the hall doorway at the same time as Flying-Officer Flaps. Not having a cap or great-coat to hang up, the bat filled in the time by a brief reconnaissance flight up the passage as far as the Mess Secretary's office, and returned just in time to accompany Flaps into the ante-room, narrowly missing his left ear.

The committee promptly went into session on bats, while the bat went into retirement in a window curtain.

Wing-Commander Blower opened the proceedings by saying blow him down, what the hell was that?

Pilot-Officer Stall gave it as his opinion that it, whatever it was, came out of Flying-Officer Flaps' hair, and therefore might be anything. Flying-Officer Flaps instantly took one of the poorest of views ·of Pilot-Officer Stall's opinion and particularly of the word "therefore." Pilot-Officer Stall said, oh, let it go, let it go, some people couldn't take a joke.

Wing-Commander Blower said, stop it, boys, and repeated his query, and Flight-Lieutenant Lyne-Shute replied that he wouldn't care to formulate an answer without some refreshment, perhaps as Flying-Officer Flaps was nearest the bell . . .? Flying-Officer Flaps fell in with the suggestion, adding that it (the refreshment) was on him (Flaps).

Pilot-Officer Prune referred back to the main subject under discussion and stated that any fool could see it was a bat: he then referred further back to the source of the query (Wing-Commander Blower) and amended his statement to the effect that he believed, sir, subject to correction, sir, that it was a bat, sir. Flying-Officer Talespin said from the glimpse he had of it it appeared to be a noctule, or *Pipistrellus noctulus*, a species which . . . Wing-Commander Blower said for the love of Mike to call it a plain bat.

Group-Captain Boost said suddenly, what was all this about a bat, there wasn't a bat, he didn't see any bat, where was this damn bat, if really a bat?

Pilot-Officer Rudder said, yes, sir, it was a bat, sir, you're quite right, sir. Squadron-Leader Undercart said he thought it was out at dispersal. Pilot-Officer Stall said, yes, by jove, he could see the little beggar, there, hanging up on the curtain, no *there*, follow his finger, *there*, where he was pointing . . .

Flight-Lieutenant Lyne-Shute requested the last speaker not to point so ruddy much, he near as a toucher had his beer over, well, mud in the eye, Flaps, old man, and he'd better drink it before some fool spilt it. Pilot-Officer Nose-dyve said it was frightfully wizard the way a bat could hang

up by the tail like that, wasn't it wizard? Pilot-Officer Prune
said it'd be even more wizard if they could hang Spitfires
up by the tail instead of having them sitting around on the
ground. Squadron-Leader Undercart said any reduction of
things on the ground for Pilot-Officer Prune to taxi into
would certainly be an advantage. Pilot-Officer Prune
refrained from comment upon this statement.

The bat here took off and did three swift figures-of-eight
over the airfield, followed by what was variously described
as an Immelmann (Pilot-Officer Stall), a half-roll off the top
(Flying-Officer Talespin), a flick half-roll (Group-Captain
Boost), frightfully wizard (Pilot-Officer Nosedyve), an
upward roll (Squadron-Leader Undercart), and something
which made him feel quite faint, here's to the bat (Flight-
Lieutenant Lyne-Shute). It was unanimously agreed, Pilot-
Officer Rudder leading, that, of course, it was a flick half-
roll, no doubt about it, the Group-Captain was quite right.

The bat continued its evolutions, maintaining good flying
speed throughout and using a lot of bank. Wing-Commander
Blower stated authoritatively that it had obviously many
flying hours behind it: Group-Captain Boost said pretty
good acro*bat*ics, ha ha: and Pilot-Officer Rudder said, Ha
ha ha, da-amn good, sir, ha ha, acro*bat*ics, ha, ha.

Pilot-Officer Prune said that, considering his cousin,
Pilot-Officer Plum, could only get in the R.A.F. as Admin.
and S.D. because he was supposed to be as blind as a bat,
then judging from the way that bat was avoiding the electric-
light-pendant barrage flying on the ceiling, Plum was wasted
where he was. Flying-Officer Talespin said it was obvious
that bats must have been trained under the hood from birth
to be able to fly blind with such manœuvrability, and Pilot-
Officer Nosedyve said they must have the most wizard sort
of gyro in their heads combining artificial horizon, rate-of-
turn indicator, and rate-of-climb indicator, to say nothing
of a very sensitive altimeter, absolutely wizard, what. Flying-

Officer Flaps said there'd have to be a compass and an air-speed indicator on the bat's instrument panel as well. Pilot-Officer Nosedyve said yes, wizard.

Wing-Commander Blower preferred to assume that the bat knew all the gen on Standard Beam Approach, and Flight-Lieutenant Lyne-Shute said that if Flying-Officer Flaps would make an approach, either standard, beam, or both to the bell, he would buy him the other half. Pilot-Officer Stall said that if operational bats used Standard Beam Approach there would have to be ground-staff bats, to play the part of Main Beacons, Inner and Outer Beacons, and so forth, transmitting dots and dashes. Pilot-Officer Rudder said how could a bat transmit dots and dashes. Pilot-Officer Prune said bats squeaked. Pilot-Officer Rudder said he'd never heard them. Pilot-Officer Prune said it wasn't him *had* to hear them, it was the homing bats coming in on the beam.

Group-Captain Boost said for heaven's sake stop all this natter about bats in general and get this particular bat out of the Mess. It had taken to doing circuits round his head, and he now thought it was requesting permission to land.

Squadron-Leader Undercart said, O.K., sir: just how does one catch a bat? Pilot-Officer Prune said in an under-tone, he'd always understood one needed a hat and a slice of bacon, and Group-Captain Boost, overhearing, asked what in hell he was burbling about now, was he nuts, who told him that? Pilot-Officer Prune said, his nurse, sir. Group-Captain Boost said he'd always thought Prune needed a nurse, but didn't know he'd actually brought one into the Service with him. Pilot-Officer Prune, blushing, said he was merely referring to an old nursery rhyme, sir, bat, bat, come under his hat, and he'd give it (the bat) a slice of bacon. . . . Group-Captain Boost said, for God's sake. Flying-Officer Flaps said, what kind of bacon, an Inner Bacon or an Outer Bacon or a Main . . . Group-Captain Boost, interrupting, said he'd had just about as much as he could stand, get the damn bat *out*. He then left the ante-room.

The bat gave a sudden burst of engine and left with him. The rest of the Committee left very hurriedly by the other door.

HENS

ON Saturday night the R.A.F. Mess, Prangmere, once again went into committee. On this occasion the subject was hens.

Squadron-Leader Undercart opened the discussion by remarking he'd heard he was being posted to another Station and was wondering what to do about his hens. Pilot-Officer Stall said what hens. Squadron-Leader Undercart said the hens he had at the back of his house, he didn't want to leave them to the next tenant, particularly the speckled one that laid so well, his wife was much attached to her.

Flying-Officer Talespin said was she going with him. Squadron-Leader Undercart said that's what he was wondering about. Flying-Officer Flaps said he supposed it depended on accommodation at the other end. Squadron-Leader Undercart said as long as she had a place to scratch, she'd be happy all day.

Flight-Lieutenant Lyne-Shute here rose to his feet and registered an impassioned objection to Squadron-Leader Undercart having referred to his wife's habits in such manner. Was chivalry in this new R.A.F. so dead that . . .

Squadron-Leader Undercart replied tersely he wasn't speaking of his wife, but of his speckled hen, and Lyne-Shute was a clot. Flight-Lieutenant Lyne-Shute said he apologised . . . had he for a moment . . . never would he . . . why, stap him, he apologised again, would Undercart join him in a noggin of beer.

Squadron-Leader Undercart said he didn't mind if he did, and Flight-Lieutenant Lyne-Shute said quickly, anyone else, too late, boys, waiter two beers.

Pilot-Officer Prune said suddenly he'd been thinking this hen business over (derisive laughter, cries of "What with?" etc.) and he thought that if Squadron-Leader Undercart was going to wangle an aircraft to fly over to his new Station . . . Squadron-Leader Undercart, indicating Group-Captain Boost in conference with Wing-Commander Blower at the far end of the Mess, said, psst, yes, he was, but Groupy didn't know it yet. Continuing, Pilot-Officer Prune said that in that case why didn't Undercart fly the hens over with him.

Pilot-Officer Nosedyve said wizard, Pilot-Officer Rudder said good show, and Flying-Officer Talespin said he (Prune) had certainly got something there. Flight-Lieutenant Lyne-Shute said it was good enough to have another beer on, let him see, wasn't it Undercart's turn, waiter, the Squadron-Leader wants you.

Flying-Officer Flaps said he could hardly wait to see the day, would Undercart carry the hens loose in the plane, because if so it'd be the funniest air crew any pilot had. Pilot-Officer Prune said he could just see the speckled hen as "Tail-end Charlie," giving warning clucks down the inter-com. if an Me. were sighted, like the hens that saved the Capitol . . . Pilot-Officer Stall said clot, it was geese. Pilot-Officer Prune said blow him down so it was. Pilot-Officer Stall said it was a wonder he (Prune) hadn't said they'd saved the Gaumont and made a job of it. Pilot-Officer Prune expressed disagreement, and Wing-Commander Blower said not to make such a ruddy row over there.

Flying-Officer Talespin said Undercart would have to be careful lest any of his hens got out of the aircraft and started flying solo, to have an Anson flying wing-tip to wing-tip with a Rhode Island Red at fifteen hundred feet would look undignified and not in keeping with Air Force traditions either.

Pilot-Officer Rudder said he had a brilliant idea. Flight-Lieutenant Lyne-Shute said that if his (Rudder's) idea was to offer him (Lyne-Shute) half a can, he (Lyne-Shute) agreed as to its brilliancy. Pilot-Officer Rudder said didn't Lyne-Shute ever think of anything but beer. Flight-Lieutenant Lyne-Shute said very rarely, waiter, a beer. Pilot-Officer Rudder said here was his idea, why didn't Undercart fly his hens over as a squadron instead of as passengers, dammit, they had plenty of flying hours behind them, hadn't they?

Pilot-Officer Nosedyve said wizard, he could just see Squadron-Leader Undercart taking off and setting course for his new Station with a squadron of hens formating on him. Flying-Officer Flaps said he wondered whether they were sufficiently hot on formation flying, he understood hens didn't practise it much, preferring to taxi about the airfield with occasional bursts of engine, say, when they saw another hen with a worm at the far end of the runway: with so little experience if they tried to fly in tight vic formation there'd be a hell of a lot of collisions.

Pilot-Officer Stall said who was talking about tight vic, over friendly territory they'd fly in line astern and if challenged would be expected to lower their undercarriages and fire the colour of the day. Flight-Lieutenant Lyne-Shute said he'd give a barrel of beer to see that, no, on second thoughts only half a barrel, beer was too precious.

Pilot-Officer Nosedyve said they ought really to fly in sections line abreast, in case of hostile hawks: instead of Blue Section and so on, one would have Speckled Section, Light Sussex Section : . .

Pilot-Officer Prune said why this assumption that they were fighter hens, far more likely they were bombers: if that speckled hen were such a good layer as Squadron-Leader

Undercart cracked her up to be, she'd probably be unable to restrain herself from parking a cookie *en route*, and if having an egg dropped on you from two thousand feet wasn't being bombed, what was, no, bombers certainly.

Group-Captain Boost here came over and said, oh by the way, Undercart was not being posted to another Station after all, and this naturally closed the discussion.

Flight-Lieutenant Lyne-Shute said all the talk had made him thirsty, waiter, a beer, and good old R.F.C. . . .

BEES

I

THE R.A.F. Mess, Prangmere, started the next week well by going into committee on Sunday evening on the subject of bees.

It began when Group-Captain Boost, entering the Mess and calling for a glass of near-sherry, pointed out severely to the Mess Secretary that there had been no honey at tea. The Mess Secretary talked convincingly about natural shortages for seven minutes, and Group-Captain Boost listened for one and a half of them. At the end of it all he said something had to be done about this damn sherry. Squadron-Leader Undercart said bright idea, solve the problem by keeping bees. Group-Captain Boost said bees had nothing to do with sherry. Squadron-Leader Undercart said no, sir, honey, sir, and Group-Captain Boost said oh, ah, yes, Undercart had taken the words out of his mouth, let bees be kept, and he supposed he might as well try another glass of this Fino Horrifico, wine type.

Wing-Commander Blower then proposed that Pilot Officer Stall be appointed Station Bee-Master. This was carried with one dissentient, Pilot-Officer Stall, who in an impassioned speech said bees were a menace, they carried far too efficient a rear-gunner, why should the Mess have bees, who wanted even one bee, let alone several . . .

Flight-Lieutenant Lyne-Shute here said thanks very much, he'd have one beer, or even several if the offer was being extended, and that Pilot-Officer Stall should speak more distinctly, for the moment it had sounded just as though he had said bee, not beer. Pilot-Officer Stall replied heatedly he did say *bee*, BEE, BEE. Flight-Lieutenant Lyne-Shute said thanks again, waiter, one bee in a large tankard, and put it down to Pilot-Officer Stall.

Pilot-Officer Rudder said the C.O.'s idea of keeping bees was a cracking fine one. Pilot-Officer Nosedyve said yes, wizard. Flying-Officer Flaps agreed, adding that sugar was necessary to sustain life. Flight-Lieutenant Lyne-Shute said there was sugar in beer, as far as *his* life was concerned. Flying-Officer Talespin pointed out that he (Lyne-Shute) was evidently under the impression he had as many lives as a cat. Squadron-Leader Undercart said two cats. Flight-Lieutenant Lyne-Shute said, laugh away, they were just jealous of people who *could* drink beer, he didn't know what young fellows were coming to, why in 1915 when *he* was in the R.F.C. in the last . . . Wing-Commander Blower said spare them, they knew it by heart.

Group-Captain Boost said he hoped the Mess bee-keeping would be instructive as well as profitable. Pilot-Officer Prune said one could learn an awful lot about everything from everything if only one could remember it. Pilot-Officer Rudder said the bees' maintenance system must be wizard, for the best authorities stated that the busy little bee im-proved *each* shining hour, showing that they ran a twenty-four-hour crash service. Pilot-Officer Prune added that they also gathered honey *all the day* from ev'ry opening flow'r, and that if they were to take the bees' system to heart the mess bar ought to run a twenty-four-hour serv . . . Flight-Lieutenant Lyne-Shute here very swiftly identified himself with the last speaker's remark.

Wing-Commander Blower said Pilot-Officer Prune had fallen for duff gen, gathering honey, to a bee, was *work*. . . . Pilot-Officer Nosedyve said what was that last word, sir, never heard of it. Continuing, Wing-Commander Blower asked how Pilot-Officer Prune would like to maintain standing patrols *all the day*. Flying-Officer Talespin said Prune was thinking only of the drones who spent their time knocking back stoups of nectar at the local, the only standing patrol a drone did was waiting outside for opening time, drones were not keen types at all to have in a Bee Squadron, and if Pilot-Officer Drone thought . . . The rest of his remark was inaudible owing to a spirited protest from Pilot-Officer Prune. Wing-Commander Blower said now, boys, chuck it.

Flying-Officer Flaps said air tactics could be learned from the Queen Bee, who had obviously studied the War Manual, Part I, for the first Queen to be air-borne immediately shot up all the other queens in their hangars, thus achieving air superiority (*cheers*), showing maintenance of the aim (*cheers*) and the offensive spirit (*cheers*), he thanked the Committee for their cheers and . . . Flight-Lieutenant Lyne-Shute said did he say *beers*, because if so, he (Lyne-Shute) would . . .

Group-Captain Boost here let in his over-ride and said for God's sake stop nattering, Pilot-Officer Stall, as O.C. Bees, was to indent forthwith for a Wing of bees with the necessary hangars and other ancillary equipment, to organise said Wing, when posted, into two operational Squadrons, allot main and satellite honey-fields after suitable reconnaissance and report progress at the next meeting, had he got that? Pilot-Officer Prune with some inconsequence pointed out that so worked the honey bees, sir, creatures that by a rule in Nature, sir, taught the act of order to a peopled kingdom. Flight-Lieutenant Lyne-Shute said that he personally had been in the act of ordering a beer, but if Prune insisted . . .

The meeting then broke up.

BEES

II

ON Monday evening the R.A.F. Mess, Prangmere, went into committee again to welcome the bees which Pilot-Officer Stall, as Station Bee-Master, had been managed to obtain that day. The meeting took place on the Main Honeyfield—the small lawn in front of the Mess—where two brand new bee hives had been installed.

The proceedings were opened by Group-Captain Boost, who said what were those damn things. Pilot-Officer Stall said those were the hangars, sir, for Nos. 1 and 2 Bee Squadrons, Prangmere Wing, just reporting under care of Miss Grimjaw, local Bee-Lady, sir, yes, that was her, sir, coming in at the gate. Group-Captain Boost said gawd what a dial, he for one was going back into the Mess. Flying-Officer Flaps said was that buzzing noise the Prangmere Bee Wing approaching in a power dive, because if so he would return to the Mess as well. Pilot-Officer Stall said the buzzing must be in his (Flaps') ears, due no doubt to drinking too much beer with Flight-Lieutenant Lyne-Shute earlier in the day, bees posted to new units never arrived by air, the procedure was as for the distribution of cased air-craft. Flight-Lieutenant Lyne-Shute said no such thing. Pilot-Officer Stall said he (Stall) had all the latest gen on bees from the Apiary Manual and Pilot's Notes and Lyne-Shute didn't know what he was talking about. Flight-

Lieutenant Lyne-Shute said he meant *no such thing as too much beer*, he *did* know what he was talking about, and not from reading manuals either, why beer was his subject. Pilot-Officer Stall said to put a sock in it, why hullo, Miss Grimjaw, no, he was not speaking to her, were those the Mess bees in those boxes?

Miss Grimjaw, Bee-Lady, was here co-opted on to the Committee and said what did Pilot-Officer Stall think was in the boxes, seagulls, should she transfer the bees to the hives right away?

Wing-Commander Blower said he'd just remembered he wanted to write a letter in the Mess: Flight-Lieutenant Lyne-Shute said he'd just remembered he wanted to order a beer in the Mess: Pilot-Officer Prune said he'd just remembered the Mess. The rest of the Committee concurred with the last speaker and set course for the Mess. The Bee-Lady said they were not to be children, there was nothing to be frightened of, they need not edge off like that. Pilot-Officer Stall, as O.C. Bees, amplified the previous statement, there was no need to take avoiding action, the Bee Squadrons would not have to make a cross-country to their hangars, they were wheeled in, so to speak, by hand. The Committee, thereupon, changed to a reciprocal course, except Flight-Lieutenant Lyne-Shute, who said he was taking securing rather than avoiding action, with a beer as the main objective.

Continuing, Pilot-Officer Stall said, the idea, chaps, was the Bee Lady puffed smoke into the boxes, the bees dashed for their respirators, found they had left them as usual in the office and so ate their emergency honey ration which, being issued on a generous scale, rendered them quite unfit for operations for a considerable period.

The Bee-Lady here produced a lot of smoke from brown paper and a bellows. Pilot-Officer Rudder said it reminded him of Flight-Lieutenant Lyne-Shute's pipe. Flying-Officer Flaps said, if so, the bees must be dead by now: compared to

Lyne-Shute's pipe, burning offal was ruddy incense. Flight-Lieutenant Lyne-Shute here returned with a beer and said Pilot-Officer Rudder could take a running jump at himself.

The Bee-Lady, who had assumed anti-bee clothing, said was the Committee ready: if Pilot-Officer Stall would hold the other box . . .

Two minutes later the Committee broke up informally . . .

At a Court of Inquiry held later that evening in the Mess, Group-Captain Boost stated he did not propose to allocate too much blame, not even to Pilot-Officer Stall for dropping the box, he personally, being on the right side of the Mess window, had been vastly entertained. The screen of flak that Flying-Officer Nosedyve put up with a handkerchief he considered most commendable, only one intruder getting past, and he understood the swelling went down after a mere week. Squadron-Leader Undercart's five-eighths seconds for the fifty yards was a notable achievement, while, if only that powerful slap of Pilot-Officer Rudder's had been bang on the target instead of being a near miss on his (Rudder's) face there would undoubtedly have been one operational bee less on No. 1 Squadron.

The fact that Pilot-Officer Prune was shot down within sight of his home base was perhaps rather reprehensible, let it be a lesson to him not to fly straight and level when enemy aircraft were about. And, as for Flight-Lieutenant Lyne-Shute, it had been an unforgettable experience to see him drop a nearly full can of beer, probably he'd never done such a thing since Richthofen last chased him, he hoped his arm would not be so stiff, as a result of enemy action, as to prevent him raising future cans to operational height. Meanwhile he called for volunteers to paint the bee hangars to-morrow in accordance with the standard camouflage scheme laid down for aerodrome buildings, unfortunately the point had escaped his mind earlier.

No names were forthcoming.

BEES

III

ON Tuesday night the R.A.F. Mess, Prangmere, went into committee once more to consider the behaviour of the 1 and 2 Bee Squadrons, Prangmere Wing, who had the previous night been installed in their new hangars on the Mess lawn.

Group-Captain Boost opened the proceedings by saying how was the Bee Wing getting along, what a day that had been, to see Squadron-Leader Undercart homing all out for lunch in the Mess with a fighter bee on his tail had been worth a million dollars. Squadron-Leader Undercart said he was glad the bee had been only metaphorically on his tail, and as for homing all out, no such thing, sir, he was merely taking normal avoiding action and had the situation well under control.

Pilot-Officer Rudder said in his opinion calm and steady nerves were needed for dealing with the Bee Squadrons, particularly when passing close to their hangars, he personally was now using the back entrance to the Mess. Pilot-Officer Nosedyve said him too by gum. Group-Captain Boost said if they couldn't get acclimatized to a few bees round the Mess it was a poor show, besides the swelling on his (Nosedyve's) jaw was going down nicely and couldn't still be painful, anyway his face looked less like a pot-bellied ostrich egg. Pilot-Officer Nosedyve said oh he said really, sir.

Flying-Officer Flaps said he also did not care for passing too close to the hangars with bees taxy-ing in and out all day and liable to make an operational sortie any minute. Flight-Lieutenant Lyne-Shute, concurring, said he certainly preferred to sit by the window and watch them through glass instead of . . . Flying-Officer Talespin said did he say through *a* glass, or just . . . Flight-Lieutenant Lyne-Shute said very swiftly that was extremely kind of Flying-Officer Talespin and his was a beer.

Wing-Commander Blower pointed out that the Bee Wing's flying discipline was lousy, only the previous night as he was leaving the Mess in the dusk, a large four-engined bee, showing no navigation lights, landed without permission on the back of his neck, having apparently failed to make its own base through faulty homing procedure. Pilot-Officer Prune, reminiscently fingering a swelling on his forehead, said with emphasis he would like to see the entire Bee Wing fitted with long-range tanks and briefed for a lengthy cross-country in search of some hypothetical field where the clover grew as big as dahlias, the general object of the exercise being that with luck they'd get out of W/T touch with their base and never never return. Pilot-Officer Nosedyve said wizard idea, chaps.

Flying-Officer Flaps said all he'd got to say was that he, gosh, what was that droning sound, there was a dive-bombing bee loose in the Mess. Flight-Lieutenant Lyne-Shute said not to jump like that for Pete's sake, he (Flaps) had upset his (Lyne-Shute's) beer, waiter again please, on Flying-Officer Flaps. Flying-Officer Flaps said, no, waiter, be damned to that, let him buy his own, there was only a drop in it anyway, he'd been had like that before. Pilot-Officer Stall, Station Bee-Master, said didn't Flying-Officer Flaps know the difference between a dive-bombing bee inside a room and a harmless reconnaissance bee outside, doing tight turns round a rhododendron while waiting permission to land and refuel.

Group-Captain Boost said he was sick of all this binding about bees who never hurt anyone unless provoked. Wing-Commander Blower said that was all very well, sir, but he (Group-Captain Boost) had been on the safe side of the window the previous night and so hadn't had the painful experience of a quite unprovoked squirt from a bee's rear-gunner. Group-Captain Boost rather stiffly said that was nothing whatever to do with it, and called on Pilot-Officer Stall to state officially whether bees deliberately took the offensive. Pilot-Officer Stall confirmed that bees did not attack without provocation, in the nice bee, sir, did not a sense so subtly true, sir, from even poisonous herbs extract the healing dew, sir, Alexander Pope, sir. Flight-Lieutenant Lyne-Shute spoke monosyllabically but plurally. Pilot-Officer Prune, again fingering the swelling on his forehead, said that let that be as it might, some bees couldn't tell the difference between a poisonous herb and him (Prune). Flying-Officer Talespin said *what* difference, and Wing-Commander Blower said now boys, chuck it, mind the furniture. . . .

Group-Captain Boost said he wished they'd stop nattering about bees, what about honey, honey, honey, which was what they started keeping bees for anyway, yes, HONEY.

Pilot-Officer Stall said ah, sir, time alone, sir, would show, sir.

DUCKS

THE R.A.F. Mess, Prangmere, went into committee on Wednesday night in order to discuss matters of considerable importance. The subject on this occasion was ducks.

Flying-Officer Flaps began it by saying now they'd got bees, why didn't the Mess keep ducks as well, there was a bit of ground at the back, he was rather partial to a nice duck egg himself. Pilot-Officer Rudder said the idea left him cold, he hated the sight of ducks, anyway, it was something about their tail unit assembly and the fact that they couldn't taxi about the airfield without rocking from side to side on their

C

undercarriages, also he didn't like the taste of duck eggs. Pilot-Officer Stall said he understood the taste depended on how you kept the ducks: if they lived on a pond the eggs tasted fishy. Pilot-Officer Prune said supposing there weren't any fish in the pond. Pilot-Officer Stall told him to put a sock in it.

Pilot-Officer Nosedyve said he'd always understood ducks had to have ponds, or at any rate a lot of water, else how could they let it roll off their backs? Flight-Lieutenant Lyne-Shute said he didn't care who had to have a lot of water so long as it wasn't him, which reminded him would Flying-Officer Flaps, who was nearest the bell—ah, thank him.

Flying-Officer Talespin said the water question depended on the kind of duck, some were so to speak Coastal Command types and needed a lot of water. . . . Flight-Lieutenant Lyne-Shute said who needed a lot of water, not to talk like that—ah, waiter, a beer. Flying-Officer Talespin, continuing, said the varieties of domestic duck were, of course, all descended from the common mallard or wild duck, *Anas boschas*, the most important breeds being the Rouen, the Aylesbury, the Peking, the Cayuga. . . .

Squadron-Leader Undercart here forcibly requested the speaker to stop shooting a line. Pilot-Officers Stall, Nosedyve and Rudder instantly associated themselves with this request. Missiles were also thrown. Flying-Officer Talespin, continuing in a louder voice, his diction being somewhat hampered by a cushion, said but there was the Indian runner duck which required very little water indeed. Flight-Lieutenant Lyne-Shute at once expressed great admiration for the Indian runner duck and said they definitely had something there, if Flaps who was still nearest the bell would oblige again, he'd show any runner duck Flying-Officer Talespin cared to name how the boys of the R.F.C. could do without water altogether as long as there was plenty of—ah, waiter, another beer.

Pilot-Officer Nosedyve said this duck-keeping business seemed rather wizard to him, they certainly laid more eggs than hens, being, he understood, operational every day, whereas hens mostly took a rest day in between sorties, doubtless for purposes of bombing up again. Pilot-Officer Rudder said yes, but hens at least always parked their cookies in the same target area, where they could be easily discovered by the egg-disposal squads, ducks evidently had pretty ropey air-bombers, releasing their loads at scattered points such as tufts of grass and other non-nest objectives, which in a large duck-drome made them difficult to find. Pilot-Officer Prune concurred, saying that, when carrying out square searches over an airfield operated by ducks, he often only found the eggs by treading on them.

Wing-Commander Blower said that was just the sort of thing he expected of Prune, crashing eggs was nothing to a chap who could crash Spitfires. Flying-Officer Flaps said if Pilot-Officer Prune could not be fitted with a de-Gaussing device, why not have duck-egg-detectors like they did for minefields, one of the sapper types would show them the form.

Squadron-Leader Undercart said that if ducks were really in the habit of jettisoning their bomb-loads regardless of whether they were over the target or not, it looked as though something were wrong with their bombing panels, did they, for instance, ever release unintentionally when airborne? Flying-Officer Talespin said no, but they frequently did when water-borne. Pilot-Officer Prune said he'd never heard of Coastal types doing that, did they float, the eggs, of course, not the ducks, he knew the answer to that one. Flying-Officer Talespin said no, they were in the nature of mines, sinking to the bottom and only rising when no longer live.

Flying-Officer Flaps said if ducks then had no more sense than to lay mines in friendly waters, he for one was against the whole idea of the Mess keeping them. Pilot-Officer Stall said yes, who'd look after them. Wing-Commander Blower said that if, mark him, *if* ducks were kept an officer would be definitely appointed in a supervisory capacity. Pilot-Officer Prune said what officer, and Wing-Commander Blower said the officer who would be detailed by him (Blower) for the job. He then let his eye rove inquiringly round the meeting and all present affected to read papers and magazines, Pilot-Officer Prune even going so far as to bury himself, for about the first time in his life, in an official Training Memorandum with a blue cover.

Pilot-Officer Nosedyve summed up the feelings of the meeting by saying perhaps the whole idea wasn't so wizard after all, he now took a poor view of keeping ducks. All present under the rank of Squadron-Leader heartily concurred.

At this point Group-Captain Boost entered and said he'd been thinking the Mess should try keeping ducks, what did all present think of it. Pilot-Officer Rudder at once said dashed good idea, sir, Pilot-Officer Nosedyve said wizard, and all present under the rank of Group-Captain heartily concurred.

Wing-Commander Blower once more let his eye rove inquiringly round the meeting, which broke up in haste. Flying-Officer Flaps, being last out of the door, was formally appointed Duck-field Controller and was told to get quacking.

STORKS

THURSDAY night saw the R.A.F. Mess, Prangmere, again in committee, the subject this time being storks. Pilot-Officer Nosedyve opened the discussion by saying that when circling the airfield that morning preparatory to making his usual wizard landing he nearly collided with a heron. Wing-Commander Blower said was he certain it was a heron. Pilot-Officer Nosedyve said there was nothing else it could be with legs like that. Squadron-Leader Undercart said it might have been a stork, storks had legs like that too, did he happen to notice if it was carrying a Little Bundle. Flying-Officer Talespin here said that the common stork, *Ciconia alba*, was not indigenous to Britain, its normal habitat being the European continent: it was, however, closely allied to the heron, also to the spoonbill and ibis. . . . His speech continued.

Pilot-Officer Nosedyve, addressing Squadron-Leader Undercart above and through Flying-Officer Talespin's speech, said storks were mostly white, sir, with a red spinner and a black tail unit, this bird had normal camouflage, and so obviously was not a Coastal Command type, which a heron was.

Flying-Officer Flaps said could he hear any bad engine rattle, storks he had always understood made a terrible clattering with their bills. Pilot-Officer Nosedyve said how the ruddy hell could he hear anything above his own engine. Wing-Commander Blower said if storks' bills were anything like the size of Flight-Lieutenant Lyne-Shute's bills at the bar each month they should easily be heard above a four-engined heavy bomber.

Flight-Lieutenant Lyne-Shute, awaking from a brief zizz, said did someone mention the word bar, was it time for a noggin? Squadron-Leader Undercart said with some people it was always time for a noggin, but at the moment the subject was storks, Pilot-Officer Nosedyve had apparently formated on a stork when coming in to land. Flight-Lieutenant Lyne-Shute said half a minute, more important business, waiter, a beer, now what was all that about storks?

Pilot-Officer Rudder said storking of talks, he meant talking of storks, what did they do with those long legs when flying? Pilot-Officer Stall said surely an undercarriage that size must be folding and retractable. Flying-Officer Talespin said no, they let them stream out behind, rather like towing a drogue. Pilot-Officer Stall said with an undercarriage constructed on those lines landing must be very difficult, he for one wouldn't care to fly any kite with an undercart about half as long again as itself, there'd be no future in it at all.

Wing-Commander Blower said nonsense, storks even landed on roofs and that was more than any of those present could do—except, of course, Pilot-Officer Prune, who did it accidently but frequently—why storks' hangars were even built on the tops of roofs. Flying-Officer Flaps said but probably they lived on roof-tops specially to facilitate handling their under-carriages, rather than in spite of them, they could taxi down the slope for take-off and up the other slope for landing, this latter preventing the stork over-shooting and having to go round again.

Flight-Lieutenant Lyne-Shute said that as the waiter seemed to be going round again he'd have the other half.

Pilot-Officer Prune said the thing that puzzled him about storks . . . Flying-Officer Flaps said did anything puzzle Prune, why, he always understood that he (Prune) knew everything. Pilot-Officer Prune said, har, har, har, har; very funny. Flying-Officer Flaps said it definitely was. Pilot-Officer Prune said in his opinion Flaps was a clot. . . . Wing-Commander Blower said now, boys, and Squadron-Leader Undercart said let him (Prune) stop nattering and get on with what he was going to say. Pilot-Officer Prune said blow him down, now he had gone and forgotten.

Pilot-Officer Nosedyve said that what struck him as so wizard was all the heavy bombing work storks must put in, absolutely wizard. Squadron-Leader Undercart said what heavy bombing work. Pilot-Officer Nosedyve said all those operational trips carrying babies, he didn't know what the annual world birthrate was, but it must mean a maximum effort job for all stork squadrons every night, it really *was* wizard. Pilot-Officer Stall said by gum, yes, and no help from the Pathfinders either, because babies had to be dropped at scattered points. Pilot-Officer Rudder agreed, adding that the nearest that storks had probably ever got to a concentration raid must have been in 1934 at Fort Callender, Ontario.

Wing-Commander Blower said on the other hand one had to consider the bomb-load in relation to the weight of the aircraft, babies he was credibly informed by his wife were normally about eight pounds, and an eight-thousand-pound cookie would therefore be smaller in comparison to the weight of a Lancaster, which must weigh more than a thousand times a stork, let him see, a Lancaster weighed, no, better start with the stork, assuming a stork weighed about . . . The last speaker here relapsed into silence with a paper and pencil.

Pilot-Officer Rudder said accurate identification of the aiming point before parking the squawkie was very necessary, but at this point the entrance of Group-Captain Boost brought the Committee meeting to an abrupt close.

Flight-Lieutenant Lyne-Shute said he was tired of listening to all this stork, waiter, same again please, he would now tell them a real story about the R.F.C. in 1915. . . .

At this point the meeting dissolved automatically.

PART II

OTHER TALES

FLIGHT-LIEUTENANT FUSELAGE AND
SIR FRANCIS

FLIGHT-LIEUTENANT FUSELAGE and young Mrs. Fuselage had taken a little house a mile from the aerodrome with a little patch of ground behind it. Flight-Lieutenant Fuselage wanted to use the Patch to grow onions and Mrs. Fuselage wanted to use it to keep ducks. They argued the toss for a week and finally came to one of those compromises so essential to happy married life. They agreed to keep ducks.

So Fuselage went to a local farmer and invested in six ducks. He didn't know anything about ducks, a fact the farmer discovered in time to point out that the market price of ducks had in a manner of speaking recently gone up. He also for various plausible but indelicate reasons sold Flight-Lieutenant Fuselage a rather fierce-looking drake.

On her husband's triumphant return Mrs. Fuselage did a spot of raised-eyebrow stuff. Six ducks, she thought, had been agreed upon; why the drake? Drakes didn't lay eggs. Drakes, moreover, if they were anything like other representatives of their sex, cost a lot to feed. She hadn't intended to have a drake and she didn't want a drake.

Fuselage, fully conscious of the fact that he hadn't intended to have a drake and didn't want a drake either, replied stiffly that after considerable thought he had decided to buy a drake because he wanted a drake. He asked his wife how, supposing she were a duck—which, he tactfully added just in time, she of course was—she would like to live with five

other ducks and not a single man about the Patch. Mrs.
Fuselage said, oh well, if he put it like that, and hastily
changed the subject by christening the drake Sir Francis.

Sir Francis and his wives soon settled in. The ducks
achieved several eggs. Sir Francis bossed them around
generally and was never, never late for meals. In his eagerness
to get at the eats he always trod in the trough and frequently
on one of his wives' necks as well. Both from the point of
view of table manners and of sympathy for women's rights,
Mrs. Fuselage began to dislike him intensely.

Her dislike turned to hatred when Sir Francis developed
a new habit. At any time from 5.0 a.m. onward he would
wake up and feel a desire for light conversation. He would
call each of his wives in turn loudly by name till he had
roused the whole harem, and then they would all chew the
fat together for about two hours. He had a strong, carrying
voice and as a result he generally woke Mrs. Fuselage along
with the first wife, and Flight-Lieutenant Fuselage with the
second or third. From then on at least four or five of them
were talking at once, frequently very heatedly, and sleep for
the Fuselages was impossible. After a week of it Flight-
Lieutenant Fuselage confessed to his wife that buying Sir
Francis had been a bit of an error. Mrs. Fuselage replied,
good, then we'll eat him, and help out the week's rations.

It's one thing to decide on roast duck (or drake); it's
another to initiate the preliminary stages, such as killing said
drake. For three evenings in succession did Fuselage go
resolutely out to the Patch, while Mrs. Fuselage waited,
fingers in ears to avoid hearing Sir Francis' last words.

The first evening Fuselage returned after ten minutes and
said, yes, he'd caught Sir Francis but he'd let him go again;
if the way to kill a duck was to wring its neck, then he wasn't
the man for the job: it needed somebody who was used to
wringing a thick length of garden hose. The second evening
he went out with the wood-chopper and an ugly look and

came back with the wood-chopper and a baffled look. He said one wanted more hands: two to hold Sir Francis' wings, one to hold his head, one to wield the chopper and probably a couple more as spares, to allow for wastage by miss-hits.

The third evening he went out in a resigned manner and came back in a flaming temper. He said killing a duck was altogether out of his class; he was only a simple, unskilled, ill-educated bloke who could merely fly a Spitfire. He'd have to take Sir Francis into the town and get the butcher to fix him.

Mrs. Fuselage by now had realised that Sir Francis was a big well-made bird with a chassis like a two-ton truck, and that they might get tired even of roast duck after eight successive meals. She daringly suggested that they should book Sir Francis for the following Friday dinner and ask Group-Captain Boost and his wife. It was always as well to keep in with Station Commanders and might mitigate that recent slight unpleasantness over a collapsed undercarriage due to a bad landing. Moreover, it'd be cheap hospitality.

They rang up, the Boosts were delighted, and said they both loved roast duck. So next day Fuselage took Sir Francis to the butcher. Here he was met with scorn. People, it seemed, didn't eat elderly drakes, and was Sir Francis elderly? Why, if he had a beard the end of it would be webbed by now.

But the important guests were coming, and duck was promised. . . . Guiltily Fuselage ordered and paid for a nice young duck. Paid a lot too; ducks on the slab, it seemed, cost even more than ducks on the hoof. Remembering, however, the enormous cost of Sir Francis in the first place, Fuselage consoled himself by putting him into the market to be auctioned next day.

The meal at least was a success. But it could hardly be called cheap hospitality. For whatever value Sir Francis had had in the farmer's eyes must have been sentimental only. In the open market elderly drakes were a drug. He fetched 9d. of which sixpence (minimum) was the market toll and 2d. the auctioneer's commission.

And next morning at five, and for many mornings after, the senior duck would wake up and cry for her departed lord. This in turn would make the others cry. One crying duck is bad; six crying ducks are hell.

They were resold to the farmer, and Fuselage discovered that the market price of ducks, like that of drakes, had, in a manner of speaking, quite recently gone down. The Fuselages now grow onions on the Patch. However onions affect human beings, they don't make each other cry.

PILOT-OFFICER PRUNE IN THE AIR MINISTRY

PILOT-OFFICER PRUNE, R.A.F., is a Caged Bird. That is to say, he is temporarily non-operational. In other words, he is for the moment "off flying." In point of fact, he has just been appointed to the A-r M-n-stry. To the K——y branch, or "House of Ill-Fame"; the W——l Head Office is the "House of Shame."

In both houses, however, you will find Caged Birds—operational officers for the moment non-operational. They sit in mournful attitudes at unfamiliar desks, feebly trying to deal with the masses of paper by which the war is really run, if not won, and longing for the day when they can once more scour, Valkyrie-like, the vast spaces of the blue empyrean—well, *fly*, if I may coin a phrase. At times they sigh so deeply that papers whirl out of the trays in the slipstream; at times a foot moves pathetically forward under the desk as in imagination they apply a little more right rudder:

at times a hand gropes forward to the ink-pot and tests for "tanks full." People coming into the room and catching Caged Birds at this sort of thing have been known to burst into tears at the sheer pathos of it all and stumble blindly out again. Ah, if only one could set them free, let them soar once more—even, for old time's sake, give them a toy under-carriage to forget to put down!

Well, Pilot-Officer Prune has reported for duty and has been given a small office of his own. Its furnishings are a desk, two chairs and a telephone. Its decorations are a notice telling how to follow the red arrow in case of an air raid, and a comic strip (*circa* 1932) torn from a daily paper by a long-forgotten hand and pasted on the wall. Pilot-Officer Prune has looked at it quite a bit and is still puzzled by the amazing effect upon one protagonist of an extremely feeble retort by the other. The fellow has leapt two feet up and five foot back, his hat has left his head like a rocketing pheasant, and from his body visible waves of astonishment and consternation are shooting in all directions like Aurora Borealis. The general effect is of one suddenly shot through the heart at close range. What would happen, thinks Prune, if someone suddenly told him a really good joke. Why, it'd be wanton murder.

On Pilot-Officer Prune's desk are the tools of his new trade—a red-ink-pot, a black-ink-pot, pens and pencils, a ruler (which Caged Birds sometimes use as joy-sticks) an ink-pad, but no rubber stamp to go with it, and a stapling-machine, but no staples. Staples, Prune has been told by his clerk, are in short supply. There is nothing, Prune finds, one can do with a stapler without staples—except practise his Morse. He spends ten minutes calling up imaginary people on his stapler and telling them very rude things.

He also has a large pad, some hundred sheets thick, of Air Ministry blotting-paper. Air Ministry blotting paper doesn't blot, but is very good for drawing on while getting a wrong number and waiting to be transferred: or for writing things like, "Eve—1.15 p.m. Café Royal," and other notes of Caged Birds' duties.

In front of this is a row of trays. Pilot Officer Prune has marked one of these "IN," one "OUT," one "Work to be Done" and one "Work to be Avoided." All except the last are empty. The last has a large file in it. A Clerical Officer brought it in and Prune doesn't like the look of it. The Clerical Officer, in his turn, evidently didn't like the manner in which Prune pointedly put it into that particular tray, for in ten minutes he returns with a Higher Clerical Officer— for the Civil Service also has its ranks—who tactfully asks him if he can give a decision on the matter therein contained. His attitude is rather that of a prep-school matron trying to get a new boy to join in a nice round game with the others. Afraid lest, if he refuses, the Higher Clerical Officer may go away and return with a Higher Clerical Officer Than That, Prune says he'll tackle it.

The file is a bulging, gravid affair with a band round its middle, and Prune at once christens it "Goering." He then starts to read. By lunch-time he is only about halfway through. So far everybody imaginable except the Chaplain-in-Chief seems to have had a finger in the file and Prune wonders whether it mightn't be a good thing to "minute" "Goering" across to that department and thus ensure its disappearance for some months, to return probably at the end of the war with a reverent minute suggesting the subject matter hardly comes within the Church's purview, does it, and all flesh is grass. On further inspection, however, Prune realises that half-time has only just been called in the file and that the Chaplain-in-Chief may easily be playing in the second half.

He tackles the second half after lunch. Right at the end of "Goering" comes a final minute—obviously from the pen of a Caged Bird: obviously, too, one who was leaving the Air Ministry, shortly, anyway. It reads; "I note that everybody has *said* a lot on this subject, but has anybody *done* anything?'

Pilot-Officer Prune takes his pen and makes his first minute. He writes, "I agree."

The Higher Clerical Officer collects the file. His eyebrows go up. He deletes Pilot-Officer Prune's "I agree" and writes instead, "The foregoing comments also receive my concurrence."

Caged Birds have got to learn.

NIGHT DUTY OFFICER

BEING Night Duty Officer at the Air Ministry is an experience which leaves its mark on a man. You can always tell an officer who has recently been on night duty. He goes about warily, occasionally looking quickly behind him: he has several visible bruises: his eyelids are dropping with fatigue: and he hobbles like a life-long rheumatic. And it is all the result of night duty.

The wariness comes from the miles of pitch-black passages which you have to traverse from your office to the room where you sleep, or to the wash-place, or to the Messengers' Room, or more generally because you have lost your torch and way. The passages are pitch-black because at eleven o'clock a Messenger goes round switching off all lights—and, as far as you can gather, removing all the switches for the night as well. At least you can never find a single one later on, though you mine-sweep sixty foot of passage wall to a height of eight feet either side.

What you do find, of course, are several doors—all those which open outwards and have been carefully left half open. That's how a Night Duty Officer acquires the bruises, though if you are experienced you always go about with your arms extended *and* forearms bent. For if your arms are merely extended, a well-placed door can come unobtrusively between them and smack you on the nose. After several of these incidents you are left with an impression that your nose must be longer than your arms and this is apt to warp your life.

Of course doors are only some of the bruises. The others come from unexpected dog-legs in the passages. These are primarily put there to prevent you possibly catching any far-away helpful glimmer of light from under the door of the distant office where Mr. Perusal, a Higher Clerical Officer, is staying late to finish writing minutes which he might have done in the day if he made them less verbose, but, of course, wouldn't get paid overtime for if he did.

The position of these dog-legs varies on each floor, to prevent confusion between floors. The idea certainly works. You think you are on the fifth, for instance, but a shattering blow in the teeth which shouldn't have come till ten yards further on at once tells you you are on the sixth. Sometimes the side of the dog-leg facing you has a door into an office. These doors are always left wide open and so you grope straight ahead, till at last, vaguely wondering why someone has seen fit to leave desks and chairs and telephones out in the passage, you stun yourself on a steel filing cabinet belonging to a Group-Captain. His clerk finds blood and hair on it next morning, assumes it is attempted burglary, and at once opens an urgent file to catch the culprits.

The peculiar echoes in the passages are responsible for the continual looking over your shoulder. When you *know* you are the only person on the floor, you don't like to be followed by someone who isn't there. At two points on the sixth floor and one on the fifth you can hear him breathing two feet behind. You break into a run, are promptly knocked out by the open door of Room 681 and when you come round you dazedly ring up the police to say you've been attacked on duty, and would they throw a cordon round the building.

The fatigue and the stiffness come from a night spent in the Duty Officer's bedroom. This room is furnished with a truckle bed, a palliasse—the latter obviously filled by the Potato Marketing Board—a pillow—from the Scrap Iron Control people—two tables, a telephone, a small hard chair and four nominal blankets. Nominal because two have always been pinched, and the other two are regularly exchanged by anyone who has a more worn-out one. This, however, won't go on much longer now, unless a spider decides to turn in a web that's a little too unwieldy for his business. The palliasse and pillow, of course, no one would pinch or exchange —not even a Commando. And no one would be so callous as to take the small, hard chair; that's for the Duty Officer to get up and rest on during the night.

The telephone is conveniently by the bed, so that you don't have to get up. The light switch, however, is by the door, and as anyone who telephones wants to know somebody's number from a list, you have to get up, anyway. This, however, is a great relief and the kind thought is much appreciated.

Should anyone be really tough enough to drop off to sleep about 5 a.m., he won't oversleep. For the room has only a thin partition between it and the place where the Ministry's lady cleaners foregather on arrival at 6 a.m. to make tea and gossip. They also bang pails. Their kettle, too, has a bottom like a drum and as it hots up, this starts sounding off like intermittent pistol shots, gradually merging into a real Last War barrage, and ending in a noise like escaping steam. To be exact, it *is* escaping steam. At this point, or even earlier if the details of the lady-cleaners' past and present ailments and operations have proved too revolting, the Duty Officer gets up and faces the day with high courage, bleary eyes and a body racked with pain.

EARLY CHRISTIANS

EARLY CHRISTIANS may be seen, very early and very miserable, at any R.A.F. Station. They are the Physical Training Class awaiting the arrival of the Physical Training Sergeant. They are huddled apprehensively together in the cold light of dawn, as if waiting in a Roman arena to take part in the big event, playing opposite a team of jungle tigers. If they had any say in the matter, they'd vote for jungle tigers.

The Sergeant descends briskly upon them. He is bursting with rude health and wearing a gloating smile. He gazes hungrily at the victims for a bit, licking his lips in an anticipatory manner, and then suddenly barks out a stentorian order. Several of the weaker brethren are knocked over by blast. He tells them ominously he'll soon make MEN of them, and marches them off to the Gymnasium. Here he gloats over them a bit more, dry-washing his hands and chuckling to himself, while they stare fearfully at the instruments of torture.

There is a bewildering array of these: parallel bars for breaking the wrist, vaulting horses for fracturing the spine, hanging rings for producing obscure internal injuries, and on the wall barred racks for drawing a man out to twelve inches more than his normal length. The only humane note in the whole set-up is a Red Cross first-aid box, and that is rather too obviously and prominently displayed for mental comfort. Probably it merely contains stimulants for prolonging human endurance or bringing victims round in time for the next torture session.

The Sergeant starts off with what he calls a simple hopping exercise. He does it himself a bare three or four times

D

to show what it is and then walks leisurely round hurling insults and taunts at those Early Christians not keeping up a good standard. A hop according to him should not be less than three and a half feet. The class get more and more tired while he continues to talk, but he is quite indifferent. They would not be surprised to see him sit down with a newspaper or go out for a coffee, leaving them hopping their hearts out.

After the passage of what seems like five days, the exercise ends and the Early Christians are told to relax. It would seem an unnecessary command, but in view of what is probably to come it is difficult to carry out with composure.

They next have to lie full length face downwards and with the arms push their chests up slowly off the floor and down again. For the first few times it is so easy that the Early Christians think the Sergeant is losing his grip, but when he starts giving them the time by long-drawn-out numbers— "Fiiiiiiive . . . Siiiiiiix . . ."—they realise he's still at the top of his form.

In the double figures his voice can hardly be heard above the groaning of tortured lungs and the snapping of over-strained ligaments.

Another five days pass. . . .

Shortly before total collapse, the gang is ordered to its feet—this is in itself by now a herculean task—and told to "limber up." This, they are told, means sloshing each other about as roughly as possible—"*Put* something *into* it!" Lack of strength only prevents any serious casualties: but the Early Christian faces all wear a yearning look as they see the Sergeant standing by, alone being unsloshed. He is, however, in far too good condition for anyone to take a chance on it.

After a further five days the Sergeant introduces some complicated exercises with bars. No one sustains any major compound fracture and he gives up in disgust. He then tries the Early Christians out on the rings. It is obvious he hopes one of them will get his head through and hang himself. If anyone does, of course, it will certainly have been done deliberately, to put himself out of his misery. But none of them seems to have the courage—or more likely by then the physical strength—to do it; and once more he gives up. Besides, he has noticed that while one victim is being worked over, the rest are actually standing idle. With an evil grin, he starts "medicine ball."

This is a large ball weighing about three hundredweight. He tells an Early Christian to pick it up. Several of them move towards it; it's obviously a four-man job. He barks, "Only *one* of you: you aren't young ladies!" at them, and they gaze at each other incredulously while one wretched man approaches the ball. Sweating and panting—suspecting too that it is chained to the ground—he at last manages to get it knee high. He is then told to throw it to another man— "You 'eard. THROW IT!"

Once more incredulous glances are exchanged, but under the lash of a raucous voice and an inflexible will soon the Early Christians—all of whom feel they have been irreparably damaged internally—are heaving the mighty weight at each other.

Five more days pass, and, unbelievably, the Early Christians are dismissed. Each aching mass of torn ligaments, wrenched joints and bruised flesh totters from the arena, the weaker ones being carried out by those who are still able to stand.

The Sergeant goes off whistling and drumming on his chest. . . .

LEAF

AM I going 'ome for me three days' leaf? . . . Keh! You lissernerme! I'm not going on me leaf, that's that. . . . You 'eard! I'm *not going* on no leaf. Leastways, not 'ome. Not likely, with what they'd all say to me, Ma and Uncle Joe and Thergirl and that old battleaxe Aunt Florrie—keh, you should 'ear 'er. Proper binder, she is. Proper browns you off, she does.

Tell yer why I ain't going on me leaf. Six weeks ago I went 'ome on a forty-eight-hour pass just after I'd 'eard I was posted overseas. I wouldn't tell the folks *where,* of course. Careless talk, and as a matter of fac' I didn't know where meself. But they didn't all 'arf make a fusser me. Ma cried on the last night and Uncle Joe got well lit and kept saluting me and calling me a brave boy in blue, up to the time he started presenting arms with Ma's umberella and calling me little boy blue and 'ad to go to bed sudden: and even Aunt Florrie said she'd always wondered what use I was, but that she supposed that after all it had all been for the best, though Providence worked in mysterious ways: and as for Thergirl she was all over me, she was. 'Er 'ero, I was. Lovin' kid! Said goodbye fifteen times, each one better than the last. . . .

Well, a week or two later I gets seven days' proper embarkation leaf, and seeing the kit I've been issued with I guess I'm going to some place where brass monkeys don't do well. Thick leather things and fur-lined things and woollen things and gloves like dead rabbits—why, I 'ave to blow on me fingers and do a cabby every time I see them. And when I get 'ome they again make a fusser me, but some 'ow it's a bit different, because it seems after that last leaf they 'adn't expected to see me again. At least not on *leaf* again, Ma ses, looking sharp at Aunt Florrie, who's said something 'opeful under her breath. Still, all in all, it's not a bad leaf and me and Thergirl gets on together like when we was first engaged, till she gets worried about me getting cold where I'm going and starts a rush job on a muffler that looks like a tank track.

Of course Uncle Joe has to 'ave his bit of fun and he talks about snowballing and sliding down glassyers and living on dried pelican, till Ma starts sneezing and tells 'im to put a sock in it. Then Aunt Florrie chips in with a dirty one about a bloke she knew who lost four of his fingers from frorsbite, so I says it's lucky for me I never played the pianner as it won't matter so much, and Thergirl starts to cry at this and Ma tells Aunt Florrie to put a sock in it as well.

Then Uncle Fred changes the subject and starts in about Eskimo maidens and it's funny what hot stuff they are in spite of the cold. At this Thergirl stops crying quite quick and tells me if I dare lay a finger on one, she'll never speak to me again, and Aunt Florrie says, what with frorsbite, 'e probably won't 'ave a finger to lay. Still, all in all, it wasn't a bad leaf and they all say goodbye when I go, and Uncle Fred says send 'em a bit of ice when I get there, and Aunt Florrie says it'll come in 'andy for 'is fore'ead on Sunday mornings.

Well b'leeve it or not, I don't get sent off with the drarf after all, but get switched to a later one, which isn't 'arf a bind because they take my special kit away and give me a different lot and another three days' leaf. This time the kit is all thin shorts and moskeeter nets and 'ats like mushrooms, and it seems I'm for a place where it's so 'ot the 'ens lay fried eggs and turn into roast chicken while they're doing it.

'Course, me leaf this time is fair 'ell. Even Ma's a bit 'ipped at seeing me pop up again and Uncle Fred keeps on being funny about the flies and the sand and what to do when desert scorpions get in your pants. Aunt Florrie says never mind, the 'eat'll be practice for me for when I'm dead, which isn't funny; but even Thergirl laughs, till Uncle Fred starts talking about the Eastern maidens who hardly wear any clothes, and then she stops laughing quite quick and says sharp, so *that's* why I changed, I like 'em 'arf nekkid, do I, 'stead of decently bundled up like Eskimos. Aunt Florrie says, yes, and he'll 'ave all 'is fingers too, though of course 'e'll soon get leprosy, which is common out there, and then they won't look at 'im, so there's always a bright side to things.

Well, Ma began to cry about the leprosy and Uncle Fred goes on about the Eastern maidens worse and worse, till Ma 'as to laugh again, but Thergirl starts to cry. . . .

Well, it's a 'ell of a leaf, with them all crying or laughing at me: and I'm even glad to go back. Thergirl don't kiss me so good when I do go, and I only 'ope I get out East quick.

Well, as you know, it's all bin called off. They took me special kit away, and I'm being posted again, and I've got three more days' leaf. But I *ain't* going 'ome. 'Cos now I'm posted to Wigan, and you know what Wigan is to people. If they laughed last leaf, they'll split theirselves this, and Uncle Fred I know 'as a postcard a bloke sent 'im showing a bloke with his arms round two girls saying, "It's lovely 'ere at Wigan," and after all me and Thergirl don't want to part.

So I ain't going 'ome. I'm going to spend me leaf right 'ere staying in the Y.M.C.A., and if they change Wigan to Canada it's O.K. with me.

THE CHARMS OF MUSIC

SERGEANT GRENADE entered the barrack hut. "Anyone here know anything about music?" he roared.

Four self-conscious recruits shuffled forward. They had been in the Army long enough to know that men who could play musical instruments often got a chance to cut it a bit fat. They hadn't been in the Army long enough to know that it's safer never to volunteer for anything because there's bound to be a catch in it.

There was. Eyeing them, Sergeant Grenade said: "Good enough! Go and shift the piano from the recreation room to the Memorial Hall!"

Sycophantic and relieved laughter ensued and three of the victims moved resignedly to the door. The fourth, however, a palefaced lad, said; "Excuse me, sergeant! This piano? Do you intend us to play it?"

Sergeant Grenade explained that his intentions were his own, and that their communication to the outside world was a matter for him to decide, without prompting from any scrimshanking, knock-kneed, pasty-faced . . .

"Because," continued the recruit imperturbably, "the piano is not my instrument."

"I'm not asking you to play it; I'm telling you to shift it."

"But that, sergeant, would not require a knowledge of music, which, you may remember, you originally implied was essential."

Grenade was momentarily silent, either overwhelmed by the other's words or unable to select his own.

"Musical knowledge, sergeant, being, therefore, stipulated, it obviously follows that knowledge of the particular instrument involved is also a *sine qua non*."

"Fall out anyone who can play the sineyquaynon!" volunteered a recruit at the back, skilfully unidentifiable.

"Now look here, my lad. You stop arguing and go and shift that piano. . . ."

"But the piano not being my instrument, I should probably damage it." It seemed more of a threat than a supposition and made Grenade pause.

"What is your —— instrument then?" he asked with a hopeful gleam.

"Bells," said the pale-faced recruit.

"Bells! Of all the . . . *What* bells?"

The whole hut had suggestions. They poured in. "Dinner bells!" "Alarm bells!" "Marriage bells!" "Diving bells!" A recruit with a scientific turn of mind contributed "Decibels": a horticulturally inclined recruit, "Canterbury bells": and a recruit with religious knowledge, "Jezebels!" The unidentifiable recruit then said, "Bells of Hell!" Three others, promptly chorusses "Ting-a-ling!" and a humorous recruit hopefully inquired, "Hi-de-hi?" The answer lifted the roof. The thing was quite out of hand.

"SILENCE!" roared Sergeant Grenade. "See what you've done!" he said, almost reproachfully.

"I only said I had a knowledge of music, specialising in bells. You asked me, sergeant. I'm a campanologist."

There was a hushed silence.

"What in hell's that?"

"Knows all about campanulas," suggested the horticultural recruit.

There was another hushed silence.

Sergeant-Major Magazine here entered the hut suddenly. "What goes on?" he asked.

"This man says he's a campanologist."

Magazine was equal to it. "He's only saying that to get off C. of E. parade."

"No, sir. It means I ring bells."

"And run away before anyone answers, I suppose." Sergeant-Major Magazine was in humorous vein.

"No, sir. Church bells."

"What, a blooming sextant?" asked Grenade, as Second-Lieutenant Swordfrog put his head in at the door. C.S.M. Magazine at once effected the formal introductions. "Party! 'SHUN!" With a barrage of loud reports, the recruits snapped to attention.

Swordfrog entered. "Ah, Grenade! You looking after

fatigues?" He handed over a slip of paper. "Here's a small job wants doing up at the Mess. Get a suitable man detailed."

"Beg pardon, sir," put in C.S.M. Magazine, with the air of an experienced nurse sharing a joke about a half-witted child with a colleague, "Here's a man who says he's a campaignologist."

"Quite," said Swordfrog vaguely.

"Campanologist," said the pale-faced recruit, feeling that here was a kindred soul. "Expert bell-ringer, sir. Change-ringing. Doubles, triples, caters. Grandsire, Plain Bob, Stedman . . ."

"Oh, I see," said Swordfrog. "I—er—congratulate you. Useful man to have." He turned to the door, keeping his face as steady as possible. "Well, carillon, Sergeant-Major!" He then left hastily.

Magazine scratched his head. "Never heard him talk in that pansy way before," he said to Grenade, and with a last withering look at the pale-faced recruit also left.

Sergeant Grenade came into action again. "Get busy now with that piano! No, not you!" He detailed another man in place of the pale-faced recurit. "You'll only go and plain-bob the thing to blazes. You get back with the others."

The four men went. Grenade looked at the paper in his hand. Then he grinned. "Fall out anyone who knows anything about bells!" he roared.

Amid subdued laughter, the pale-faced recruit again stepped forward.

"I do, sergeant!"

"Well, report to the Officers' Mess and mend the ante-room electric bell. . . . And double up, you campaininthe-neckologist!"

MAE WEST AND THE WAR

SINCE the war started Mae West has caused my friend Tommy a certain amount of trouble. You see, Mae West has . . . One minute!

Before the question of libel crops up—as it looks like doing any minute—I'd better explain that Mae West is Mrs. Tommy's large grey parrot. She acquired the name from her habit of extending in a set phrase an informal invitation to acquaintances to pay her a social visit in the near future. She has, too, when you catch her in certain lights, a pleasant rotundity of curve. Also a wickedly roving eye—though she is probably merely looking round for her favourite snack, a small hot baked potato, which she deals with in an incredibly disgusting manner.

The first impact of the war on Mae West, or, rather, Mae West's first impact on the war—for almost immediately she had it well under control—was a spirited protest against the black-out. The blacking out, that is, of the particular window near which her cage was hung, so that from dawn to dusk she could survey and comment on the passing world.

After a week or so of blacking-out, Mae West got the idea that night seem to be setting in with unaccustomed abruptness these days and that she was somehow being cheated of her final hour of entertainment. So she reached out a claw unobserved and made herself a good peephole in the black paper. Later that night the resultant shaft of light, with Mae West's interested head silhouetted against it, brought a pack of wild wardens on Tommy's heels. The resultant argument about the hole wasn't helped by Mae West's suggesting helpfully at one point that they put a sock in it, and Tommy barely escaped a fine.

After that a special cover was made for Mae West's cage

and she had her own private black-out each evening. The bed-time conversation was always the same. Mae West bounced up and down shrieking "A.R.P.! Help! A.R.P.! Help!" in a high falsetto, as if she were being assaulted, till the cover was actually on, when she remarked severely, "Put out that dam' light, sir!" and Tommy had to see there were no chinks. "What's that like now, Mae?" he then asked, and Mae West replied; "Hellish dark and smelling of cheese!"

After this there was silence unless Mae West woke up suddenly after dinner and shouted, "Put out that dam' light, sir," in such peremptory tones that the Tommys leapt up and spun round the room guiltily adjusting curtains. One day they found themselves explaining to an angry warden that they thought he was only the parrot—and *that* started something all right.

Naturally, Mae West played her part in the first air-raid alarm. She was woken up and hauled off in a vile temper to the nearest air-raid shelter, where she proved a bit of an embarrassment. Like nearly all parrots, Mae West has somewhere in the dim past had a seafaring career. (So much in the dim past that Tommy swears she occasionally mentions the Glorious First of June as one who had been present at the battle.) Anyway, she immediately started to pass vitriolic nautical comments on the situation, while Mrs. Tommy tried hastily to knit her a gas-mask to damp her down. It was not till several of the more godly shelterers had left, preferring to face the unknown physical perils without than the undoubted moral contamination within, that a kindly lady with a snoring Pekinese presented Mrs. Tommy with a "Dope Pill for Your Dog—He Will not Hear the Air Raid," and things settled down.

Mrs. Tommy, flushed and embarrassed, had had half a mind to take the pill herself and slide out of the situation on a wave of happy oblivion, but finally gave it to Mae West.

With a last drowsy obscenity she passed out and didn't come round till next midday, when she obviously had a head on her like a concrete pumpkin. "Boy, what a night!" was her first comment.

Mae West also took part in the next potential air-raid. This time Mrs. Tommy had a supply of dope-pills, and with a good shot in the arm, so to speak, Mae West was taken to the shelter: but not unfortunately before she had again heard the wardens sounding the alarm on whistles. She was still pondering enviously about them when she dropped off to sleep.

The result was that so far from her taking a part in the third air-raid alarm, she *was* the air-raid alarm. Those short blasts of the whistle were right up Mae's street. She went on and on, in spite of being covered up, shouted at, muffled up, and sworn at—when she only paused to swear back and won the round every time. Finally, she was taken down to the coal cellar, where apparently she got the impression she was back in the cockpit of a three-decker at Trafalgar or somewhere, and started issuing orders to lay the ship alongside, my hearties, and prepare to board.

The wardens, however, were not at all sympathetic. It wasn't even as though Mae West had also learnt the official All Clear signal; for on the last two occasions she'd been deep in her pipe-dreams by the time that had sounded. Indeed, the wardens pointed out that for a bird of such attainments it was only a matter of time before she added the "continuous warbling note" to her repertory of sharp blasts and roused out the whole borough.

There was only one thing to do. Mae West became an evacuee. Mrs. Tommy, ranking no doubt as a "mother with baby," took her down to Sussex, where she was housed in a lone cottage miles from anywhere. Tommy doesn't think she can do much damage, as the old man who lives in the cottage is not as *au fait* with current events as a Londoner would be. Indeed, when Mrs. Tommy asked him what he thought of the war, his reply was; "Be 'un *on*, then?"

So there Mae West stayed and rusticated, occasionally extending her famous hospitable invitation to passing cows. The last time Mrs. Tommy saw her, she had acquired quite a Sussex accent. Later on, spurred to action presumably by seeing the hens of the countryside going about their business without panic, she distinguished herself by laying an egg. Probably the first genuine female parrot in captivity to lay an egg. All the parrot eggs laid in captivity are laid by parrots who for years previously have been called Dick, or Joe, or George Arliss.

Her end, alas! came suddenly. A flying-bomb came too close, Mae West squawking defiance at it all the way. But no doubt she died under the glorious impression that she had frightened this new type of aircraft into blowing itself up.

PART III

ARE YOU FEELING SPY-FEVERISH?

[*The following little discussion on espionage and how to detect it is, I'm afraid, a bit out of date. The publishers however, have insisted on having it in. They say* (a) *it'll remind people of the early days of the war—though who the hell wants to be reminded of the early days of the war I can't imagine: and* (b) *it's frightfully good, though who the hell else thinks so I can't imagine. But you know what flatterers publishers are. And after all they're only doing it, between you and me, to get a larger volume for the same money.*]

HAVE you got spy fever?

Do you suffer from a rumour on the brain?

Do you experience that feeling of denunciation on getting up in the morning?

Does anything suspicious catch you *here*?

In short, have you got spies before the eyes?

I feel I cannot do better than outline the general symptoms of the onset and progress of this disease which, at least claims many victims in certain areas. Authorities are agreed that there seems to be something in the climate of the South and East coasts that makes the inhabitants of those parts particularly vulnerable.

Talking Suspiciously

The first main symptom, you will find, is an increasing tendency to note down people who talk suspiciously, and report them to the local police. Suspicious people in this connection are as follows:

1. People speaking with a German accent.

2. People speaking with what you *think* is a German

accent. Probably it is Russian, Polish, Czech, Dutch, or practically anything, even Welsh. It all depends on your lack of knowledge of other languages than your own. The greater this lack of knowledge on your part the more suspicious people you will, of course, see and report. This may get you into trouble with the police—or even before that with the suspicious person himself, if the accent *is* Welsh.

3. People speaking with an Italian accent.

4. People speaking with what you think is an Italian accent. *See* (2) above, adding after Dutch: Spanish, Greek, Egyptian, Syrian, Aramaic and all points East.

5. People speaking with a perfect English accent. These are very suspicious; obviously German spies who speak with a German accent, or Italian spies who speak with an Italian accent—or even German spies who speak with an Italian accent and Italian spies who speak with a German accent, though in this case they're probably naturalized Swiss just making the thing more difficult—these, I say, are not going to be much good as spies. Indeed, by the law of survival of the fittest, most of them have long ago been liquidated. Note the difference between Continental liquidation, in which the resultant liquid promptly undergoes gasification as well and the subject disappears into thin air, and English liquidation, in which the subject merely disappears into a prison camp with all mod. con., better food than the majority of the civilian population, covered buses to and from work, while British workmen have open lorries, and, of course, the right to strike if they don't like the work.

Resuming, therefore, people who speak with a "perfect English accent" are probably very dangerous spies. Moreover, you can't rely on reporting all of them to the police yourself. You really need to engage a staff of trained reporters. *And* a lot more police.

6. People who don't speak with any accent, that is, people who don't speak at all, that is people who are deaf and dumb.

These are probably the most suspicious of the lot, because a really expert spy often pretends to be deaf and dumb. The idea is, you say things in front of him, thinking he can't hear, and he's able to report them to his headquarters, which you think he won't be able to do. Unless, now I come to think of it, he writes them down: but he may further be deceiving you in his ability to do this by pretending also to be paralysed from birth. Spies, however, who pretend to be deaf, dumb, and paralysed from birth, or who, indeed, in cases of extreme deception *are* deaf, dumb, and paralysed from birth, have a limited scope and are not much used nowadays. You will, though, if you have spy fever badly, not rely on this. You will find yourself saying to such a one, "I'm going to stick a pin in you," to see if he hears you; then sticking a pin in him, to see if he shouts automatically, "What the hell do you think *you're* doing?" and then running away to see if he chases after you. According to which of them he does, you can base your subsequent report to the police as to the extent of his deception. If he does all three, he's neither deaf, dumb, nor paralysed from birth, which is highly suspicious, unless he's merely a professional mendicant. If he does none of them, you can ask his pardon. He won't hear you, nor will he say, "Granted, I'm sure!" Nor, best of all, will he chase after you.

Apart from the above classes there are, to your mind, no other suspicious people.

There probably *are* no other people.

NOTE to (2) and (4) above: People speaking with what you think is a German or Italian accent. As this may mean any foreign accent whatever, you should be extremely careful where you go. Just as a dog who likes to chase a rabbit may on coming unexpectedly into a field absolutely full of rabbits suddenly throw a fit at the plethora of victims, so it is inadvisable for anyone suffering from spy-fever to visit Hampstead, or a fatal seizure may supervene. If you *must* visit Hampstead go straight to the new British Consulate in Belsize Park. They will issue you with a passport, a guide, and change your money for the local currency.

Suspicious Behaviour

The second principal symptom of Spy-feverishness is a tendency to note and report people who act suspiciously.

Acting suspiciously in this connection comprises the following:

1. Wearing a false moustache, beard and dark glasses. Now, of course, if they're so obviously false that you notice them as such, they will be so obvious that other people will have noticed them too—if you get what I mean—and the fellow will have a hostile crowd following him about. This is already hampering his line of work. So leave him to them and go and spy-hunt somewhere else.

2. Wearing a moustache and beard that look false but aren't—with or without dark glasses, false or to an oculist's prescription. In this case you will immediately find yourself wondering whether they are false or not and will take steps to ascertain this. You will probably remark to the suspect that you were just going to have a drink, perhaps he'll have one on you; and after he has had it and you are friendly, you will remark further that you were also just going to have a shave, perhaps he'll have one of these on you too. If he refuses, it's suspicious. If the barber can shave him quite clean with one stroke, it is more suspicious. If, however, the barber can shave him properly, it is extremely suspicious. Really clever spies, you are well aware, *don't* wear false moustaches and beards; they go to a secret School for Spies and grow them specially—probably under glass in the winter months.

3. Wearing a moustache and beard—to hell with the dark glasses idea, anyway: most up-to-date spies wear rose-tinted

E

spectacles!—that look genuine and *are* genuine, and above all, refusing to have a shave on you. Very suspicious behaviour this, because you will at once know that he is a real natural-bearded spy—very rare, and not often found in captivity. That part will be up to you.

4. Wearing clothes that come from Germany or Italy. You can tell this, either by close scrutiny and discovering the garments to be little strapped harnesses with tight shorts below, or long black Sicilian cloaks, or green hats with shaving brushes in them, and so on; or, in other cases, by looking at the maker's label in the top of the back of the trousers inside. To do this invite the suspect to have a drink with you, as in (2) above, but after you have reached the friendly stage suggest a bathe instead of a shave. When you are both in the water, you will find that in your usual forgetful manner you have gone in still wearing your wrist-watch. This will be an excuse for returning to put it with your clothes and then surrepititiously examining his trousers.[1] If the tab reads "Hochensteuffel Auslese, Berlin" (or "Mantocchini Gnocchi, Rome") you can be fairly sure he is a foreign spy. If the tab reads "Israelstein Bros.," he is almost certainly British, probably from Belsize Park.

5. *Not* letting highly important and secret documents get stolen from an unattended car. Very suspicious and un-British behaviour this.

6. Engaging in any suspicious occupation, such as making maps of barracks, camps or forts; making sketches of forts, camps or barracks; taking photos of aerodromes, crashed aeroplanes, tanks (exclusive of water-tanks), Home Guards, and soldiers between the ranks of Sergeant-Major and Brigadier. Below Sergeant-Major it's probably only Press. Above Brigadier it's only flattery—and of no value to the enemy, anyway.

7. Engaging in any occupation that *looks* to you suspicious,

[1] Unless in *his* usual forgetful manner he has gone in still wearing these.

such as making maps of towns, rivers, golf-courses, whether full-size or miniature; making sketches of villages, churches, ruined castles, or oldest inhabitants (whether full-size or miniature); taking photos of landscapes, trees, pretty girls bathing, houses, more pretty girls, this time sun-bathing ("Gaw! what a peach!"), Jack driving the Austin; Mum, Dad and Aunt Muriel at picnic, self at Bognor Regis, shutter worked by long string.

8. Showing lights. This is invariably highly suspicious—unless it is someone quite innocent who *absolutely* forgot to put their black-out curtains down in a room they *hardly* ever go into after dark, which might happen to anybody—as you yourself explained to the Warden only last week.

9. Signalling at night. This is generally done by driving a car along a road so that the lights flicker through trees a mile away and can be seen by people two miles away. Though nearly always in incomprehensible code, it is occasionally in German, but this depends on the kind of trees used. Pines, for instance, do German very well, as spies know. Oaks do Italian, and gorse is just right for Japanese. In most cases, it is invariably recognisable as a spy signalling. Really clever spies, however, frequently manage to make their signalling look exactly like the lights of a car two miles away flashing through trees one mile away. There is probably a secret school where they are trained to do this.

10. Asking the way. This is considered frightfully suspicious behaviour, particularly by the famous[1] General Bloodworthy, whose dictum on the subject I quote. "If a feller's *English*, dammit, he ought to *know* the way about his own country, even without signposts. *I* know every inch of the country round about. Asking the way, indeed! . . . What's he want to know for? . . . Up to no good! . . . I mean, feller's bound to be a spy. . . . Feller ought to be *shot!*"

11. *Not* asking the way. "Feller's a stranger—at least *I've*

[1] Famous, that is, in my village.

never seen him round here (General Bloodworthy again), and there are no sign-posts. So how does he *know* just where to go? Answer me that! Wait, I'll tell you! Because he's got a secret *map*. They pose as tourists before the war, and get them. Now thousands of copies have been made and·he's got one in his boot. Up to no good! . . . I mean, feller's *bound* to be a spy. . . . Feller ought to be shot!"

Parachutists and How to Treat Them

I shall now deal with Parachutists. Or rather, tell *you* how to deal with them; the odds are that I shall be elsewhere at the time. What I mean is, in all the fully authenticated cases of parachutists landing in England, the man who told me about it for an absolute fact turned out on questioning to have been himself elsewhere at the time.

Now it seems that paratroop chutes . . . I mean, parachoop trutes . . . that is, paracroup toots. . . . You know, I don't think my teeth can be in properly; I'll start again! It seems that *parachute troops* fall into four classes.

1. The parachutist who lands in disguise and hopes the countryside will absorb him. First of all, his disguise, it has been well drilled into us all, will be either postman, clergyman, or nun. Nothing else. If you see a milkman in a lonely field disentangling himself from a parachute, he cannot really be a parachutist disguised as a milkman because there is no such thing. He is therefore a milkman disguised as a parachutist—probably a rather ignorant milkman secretly visiting the source of supply to see how the stuff is really made.

Now the parachutist in disguise is very easy to detect, for the simple reason that his line of work necessitates his landing in remote country districts. Disguised as a postman, therefore, he hasn't a chance, because everyone in any remote country district knows the postman and his business as well as he knows theirs. The fellow won't get far before some child pipes up: "Ma, whatzappened to Postman Hodge's face 'smarning?" and they'll notice it's gone all intense and palely brutal, instead of the usual genial vermillion, and that's the end of him.

Disguised as a clergyman, his activities will be equally hampered, chiefly because his natural instinct will be to avoid talking to anyone he meets for fear of being detected. This will at once be noted as suspicious behaviour and result in his capture. It is well known that no clergyman in the remote English countryside can ever resist trying to get into conversation with everyone he meets, and, if a favourable opportunity presents itself, touching him down for something for the Organ Repair Fund.

The nun disguise requires a little more definite action on your part. Make an excuse to examine his (or her) arms and see if they're hairy.[1] If they are, you can arrest him as a parachutist because the few real nuns who just happen to have hairy arms, poor dears, have never dared venture out of their nunneries since the first week after the war, when the story started. If they aren't hairy, of course she's a real nun and you'll probably be arrested yourself—whatever excuse you made for looking at them in the first place.[2]

2. The parachutist who lands as himself, pinches a fellow's clothes and starts out to find his way to the nearest railway station for the purpose of sabotage. Being, I repeat, in the country, you needn't bother about him. He won't get far. I know from experience the kind of answer he'll get, for instance, if he asks the way from nine people out of ten in *our* village. (The tenth will be Old Gummidge, who is deaf and will only give him a blank stare.)

It'll go like this. First: "The *railway* station?" repeated in various accents of surprised interrogation, as though the

[1] Dropping a cigarette, or a rosary, or something is one way. Asking to see his (or her) vaccination marks is another.

[2] And particularly if it was vaccination marks in the wrong place.

inquiry had been for some place like Chestnut Street, Philadelphia. After a lot of this at last comes: "Oh, you mean the railway *station*," as though the chap had been speaking in code.

Then will follow this: "You goos straight down there to Codger's Cottages and then turn left up Mill Lane to that corner where Aylett's straw stacks used to be six years ago, and then over the stile into Marston's Four Acre, and—well, that is, if so be you want to go by the footpath, but mebbe you'd better take the road, so don't go to Codger's Cottages at all, but turn up the second side road at Haye's Barn. . . ." This is liable to go on for hours—even if the parachutist tries to break away, he'll be followed up the street—and other people will join in helpfully with different directions, till the fellow is practically a nervous wreck. So far from sabotage, all he'll want to do is to charter a private plane and go straight back home.

3. The parachutist who doesn't ask the way but is reckoning to go by the signposts. Don't bother about him either; he'll be in just as bad a fix, because he'll find that they've all been removed. Then while he is standing at a lonely crossroads trying to figure out whether Dimblebury Parva is to the left or the right, some passerby who's equally puzzled and has been looking for someone to question for half an hour, will come up hopefully and ask *him* the way to Little Wigglingtoe (pronounced Woo). Naturally, the parachutist won't reply that he is a "stranger in these parts himself," because he'll think it will give him away. And that's just where he'll be had, because it is well known all over England that when, after looking half an hour, you do at last find someone to ask the way from he invariably *is* a stranger in those parts himself. So when the parachutist tries to pass it off by saying, "Yes, it's down that road," he'll be suspected at once. The other man will report him when he reaches the next village and within a bare couple of hours the village

constable will puff up on a bike and ask him, now now what's all this here? . . .

4. The parachutist who lands in uniform, armed to the ears with sub-machine guns, bicycles, overalls, pistols, Verey lights, Catherine wheels, iron rations, explosives, and who, if he survives the landing, which seems doubtful, makes his way to the nearest lonely cottage, knocks on the door and asks for a drink.

Which brings me to my next section. So following on *Parachutists and How to Treat Them* we come to—

Parachutists and Whether to Treat Them

As we have seen, a parachutist whom you encounter wandering about the countryside will, if left alone, more or less ultimately solve himself. But if a parachutist encounters *you*—say, by appearing at nightfall at your cottage door and asking for a glass of water (*wasser*), or wine (*wein*), or even beer (*bier*)—the problem is quite different. It is now not so much how to treat him as whether to treat him at all.

Well, there are various ways of dealing with the situation.

1. Make certain he *is* a parachutist. You do this by studying his appearance closely. If he is not in disguise, he will be wearing a helmet with a winged badge and two chin-straps—in case he falls on his jaw when landing and breaks one of them—a rolled cape, funny sort of overalls, binoculars, a large Lüger pistol, a small automatic, bombs, a dagger, a folding bicycle, a sub-machine-gun and a good deal of casual explosive. Oh, and boots that for no ascertainable reason lace up at the sides.

Now, while possession of one or two of these adjuncts might be explained,[1] or not particularly noticed by you, a combination of the whole lot is sure to catch the eye. You will then perhaps come to the conclusion that the costume

[1] Many hikers nowadays carry folding bicycles, in order to cheat on lonely roads when they think no one is looking.

is a trifle unusual for the English countryside. It is quite possible that from this you will deduce, and correctly, that he is a German parachutist.

The next thing then is to disarm him, or as much of him as possible. So put on your best disarming smile and say hospitably in answer to his request for refreshment: "Why, sure! Step right in, stranger, and I'll rustle up sump'n!" (Don't ask me why you're apparently a stage American; I just wouldn't know! Possibly it's just dat ole American hospitality. Or, maybe, on second thoughts, you aren't American, but are trying to make him believe he's landed in the States by mistake. In which case he will realise he hasn't got any American currency and . . . Really I don't think we need pursue this line further, do you? I don't know how I got into it, anyway.) Perhaps you'd better just say instead; "Certainly! Sit down and make yourself comfortable while I get some *bier* (beer)."

By the time you come back from the kitchen you will find that he has taken off his belt—for no true German can make himself comfortable for beer-drinking without removing his belt—and as this will be carrying the Lüger pistol and the sub-machine-gun, you are a fair way on towards getting him demilitarised. There are still, however, all the other things, but if you offer him another beer, he will almost certainly take off his bombs, because while they nestle snugly to the figure in their special pockets, a fellow can't go on drinking beer and expect things like bombs still to nestle snugly to the figure.

Next, on the plea that you want a knife to cut him a bit of cake, you may get the dagger, but there is still the automatic pistol and the hidden explosive, and you will by now be realising that what you really need is the assistance of a fairly large Disarmament Commission. At this stage, some favour touching him off with a match, or detonator, if you have one handy, but the best thing is to offer him a third glass of beer and put rat-poison in it. An undertaker and a bomb-disposal squad can between them do the rest.

2. If the fellow who comes to your door and asks for that glass of water (*wasser*), wine (*wein*), or beer (*bier*), is *not* in uniform, the first thing still is to try and find out whether he is a German parachutist or not. Tramps in the country have a habit nowadays of pretending to be parachutists in the hope of getting a glass of beer (*beer*), wine (*wine*), but definitely not water (*water*). If he gets this last, you'll know at once from his language which he is. No German parachutist, however well-trained, has yet learnt enough to imitate an English tramp being offered a glass of water. So you can assume his innocence and send him away—though you'll still hear him telling the world what he thinks of you all down the lane.

3. Even when you know your visitor is not a tramp, you will still be doubtful as to whether he is actually a German parachutist, particularly if he speaks good English without the trace of an accent—except, of course, an English one—so here is one sure way of telling. Make an excuse to look at his back.[1] If he has several cords and masses of silk still attached to his shoulders, it is a parachute and he is a parachutist. You should in that case at once point out the parachute and offer to relieve him of it. He will be very grateful and so will you. It's wonderful how many curtains, sheets, pyjamas, silk handkerchiefs, and sets of undies a parachute—which is always the *best* silk—will provide. Once you have secured it, you can give him his drink with rat-poison in it with a clear conscience; like other well-brought-up people, you no doubt have an aversion to robbing the dead.

4. If he hasn't a parachute tied on him and of course still

[1] To do this, go outside the door and walk round behind him. If he doesn't like this and keeps turning round to face you, invite him into the house, saying politely, if you are a man: "After you, sir!" If you are a woman he, being a German, will go in first naturally. Either way you'll see his back.

speaks good English, the problem is a little more difficult. You must now try and trap him. Invite him in, saying you'll get him a drink, and suddenly ask: "Dry Martini?" If he replies, as he probably will, that he'll only have one of them, thank you, well only one to start with, you will have caught him out. Go off and mix some Martinis and put the rat-poison in without more ado. In the first one only, of course: silly to spoil *three* Martinis.

5. All the above implies a certain waste of drink on your part, and you may decide not to treat him, but to trap him all the same. In this case say you have nothing in the house, but you can direct him to the nearest pub. He'll naturally say what's its name and what direction. You just say: "Links. Near the golf-course." There are golf-courses all over England and frequently the pubs near them are called the Links Hotel, so it's all quite plausible. But if without any further direction from you, he turns off to the *left*, you'll have caught him again, for "*Links*" mean "left" in German. (Neat, hey?) Then all you have to do is nip secretly along with your rat-poison to the nearest pub in that direction, and bribe the barmaid to put it in his beer when he arrives.

By the way, I should have said at the start that the whole answer to the problem whether to treat German parachutists is, "Yes; with rat-poison. It's really the only thing for them."

Tracking Down a Master Spy

I now come to the real crux of my little discussion. We've dealt with suspicious behaviour and parachutists, and in fact all the ordinary run-of-the-mill "hand-over-the-papers-or-else" spies. Now I'm getting you on to Something Big—the Master Spy and How to Track Him Down.

The very first thing to do in tracking down a Master Spy is to know what a Master Spy is. It's like, say, elephant-shootin' in this respect: the chap who goes out after an elephant and comes back just in front of a fairly fast rhinoceros or carrying a brace of *'m't'pala*[1] obviously hasn't studied his subject. But whereas you can get a good idea of what an elephant looks like from books[2] before settin' out shootin', this is quite impossible in the case of a Master Spy. It's not the slightest use, for instance, looking up under "Spies" in the Telephone Buff Book: they aren't listed there.

In the spy game, secrecy is of the essence; and a Master Spy's address is generally something like "XQ/41. 6.0 p.m. nr. Arg. Pb. W.C.1," while he probably has about at least four telephone numbers, three of which are unknown to anyone except (or sometimes including) himself, and the fourth is permanently "out-of-order." I mean, you can see what you're up against. I mean, Privacy—not to say Reticence. So if you rush into the thing baldheaded you're likely to waste a lot of valuable tracking-down time and find in the end that, so far from having bagged a Master Spy, all you've got is an insignificant Acting Unpaid Lance-Spy, or a young recruit spy, or even no spy at all, but just a Mr. Jno. Fettlewether, Family Butcher, of Hammersmith Broadway.

I will now give you some pointers about Master Spies.

A Master Spy in general can be either normal or abnormal. A normal Master Spy's chief characteristic is Sinister Mystery, of which he wears the air—sometimes, however, carrying it in the tenor or bass for a change. He also wears impeccable linen and will live in an enormous house, alone except for a large staff of servants, confidential secretaries (who are so confidential it takes him all his skill to worm anything he wants to know out of them, such as what time

---

[1] A dear little native deer possessing hardly any points in common with an elephant. You can't carry a brace of elephants, for example.

[2] A most useful volume is *The Tots' Animal Alphabet* (5¾ inches by 12 inches, 26 pp., 6d. net, illustrated). Published by Messrs. Kiddiebookie Press, Ltd. The information required will be found on the fifth page.

dinner is), a few relations, some tough-looking Indian servants and his grandmother. She also frequently wears a simple old-fashioned air of Sinister Mystery in muted bugles. Probably he gets it from her.

He is visited after dark by young and beautiful women, but I hasten to add there is none of That Sort of Thing. His character is blameless, his morals, like his linen, impeccable. He would not steal a single kiss from any one of these frippets: all he ever steals from them is perhaps a simple little plan of a new battleship. He doesn't—and this is his secret—do any spying himself, any more than a Big Executive does his own typing. He pays others to do it, and if he can get the doings off them without dipping into the petty cash, well, it's that much extra gravy.

The normal Master Spy, you will observe, therefore is quite noticeable, once you have run across him. All his neighbours will have noticed the Goings On and will be ready to talk about them—though I'll bet anything you like they put a wrong interpretation upon those after-dark visits. Battleship plans, my foot, Mrs. Winter of "The Acacias" will say scornfully.

The real trouble is you can't pin anything on the Master Spy. His life may be mysterious and sinister, but the police have nothing against him. He's probably a member of several good clubs, and no glittering function is complete without him. Many a hostess, indeed, has had to go through the evening with an incomplete glittering function because he forgot the date. It was pencilled on his cuff and he changes his impeccable linen so frequently that the Laundry Manager often turns up at parties in his place. In fact, the Laundry Manager is getting to be quite a well-known social figure, and no glittering function is compl . . . But we are getting away from the point.

The other type of Master Spy is the abnormal. He never wears an air of Sinister Mystery. (If ever he had one, he hung it up in the back-hall coat-closet.) He wears more probably a bowler hat, a straggling moustache, and pince-nez and looks just like you or me. Well, say, you; because I've got horn-rimmed glasses, no straggling moustache, and haven't seen my bowler hat since my Aunt Euphemia's funeral. (Maybe, by the way, *that's* where it still is; under the third pew on the right in St. John's Church. I must remember to look next time I'm passing.)

What I mean in calling this sort of Master Spy abnormal is that, unlike the previous type, he is the last person you would ever suspect of being a Master Spy, though up to the neck in all sorts of personal spying. Wherever a new tank is being designed, or a new aeroplane tried out or new harbour defences made, somehow or other he manages to be among those present. He's lost his way, or missed the 8.20 'bus, or is looking for a cousin in the dockyard or whatever his excuse is—and with that little straggling moustache, to think of him in connection with spying is so laughable that you don't think of it. If you did, of course, you'd only laugh. Yet all the time he is pacing out distances, or accurately storing up details behind those innocent pince-nez, or photographing things with the third button of his waistcoat—it's a camera, of course, and when left unbuttoned takes quite good likenesses

Well, now I think you're all reasonably well equipped for the early days of the next war. Let's hope to God I'm not there to have to try and see a funny side to it.

PART IV

SALUTING AS IT SHOULDN'T

ABOUT halfway through the War to End Wars to End
War a Member of Parliament asked a question in the
House about saluting in London streets. He seemed to
deplore the fact that it wasn't being Done As It Should.
Laxity, he considered, had crept in.

Now at the time many of us had noticed the same thing.
But none of us exactly deplored the fact that laxity had
crept in. Life in London would have been pretty tough if it
hadn't.

Consider:

The strict rules are that every non-commissioned rank
must salute every commissioned rank, no matter of what
service, and junior officers must salute senior—except that
subalterns, and their equivalents, do not salute captains, a
point which has always been a sore one with newly-pro-
moted captains. And all salutes must be acknowledged, the
official acknowledgment being exactly the same as the salute.

Well, assuming no laxity whatever, let us take a bit of
Piccadilly about lunch-time sometime in 1942—a bit where
an Air Vice-Marshal, say, with a Royal Armoured Corps
Corporal a dozen paces behind him, is going one way, and
a Captain of the Royal Navy, with a Second Lieutenant the
same distance behind, is going the other. They approach.
This is what happens, assuming, as we said, no vestige of
laxity.

The Captain salutes the Air Vice-Marshal with strict
correctitude, that is, for three paces before passing him and
three paces after—at which point he has rapidly to start
acknowledging the salute of the Corporal. Meanwhile the

Air Vice-Marshal, who has just finished acknowledging the Captain's salute, is in action with the Second Lieutenant: and the latter has no sooner disengaged than he in his turn is at grips with the Corporal, for whom, poor devil, the whole encounter means twelve solid paces at the salute.

By the time the thing has died down, in fact, saluting between pairs has been going on for some eighteen paces, two pairs being simultaneously at it for six of them. As at the same time correct saluting means the elbow being out at right angles to the shoulder and both participants not looking where they are going, but straight into each other's eyes, the general effect is about as devastating to other users of the pavement as a tank attack.

And remember that's only for a bit of Piccadilly with four uniforms; in 1942 there would certainly have been a lot more uniforms in that bit at lunch-time, and in 1942 there were also lots more bits of Piccadilly. London, in fact, would have been a shambles *if* saluting had been Done As It Should.

So naturally it was being Done As It Shouldn't. And as with any other departure from the strait and narrow path, the deviations were numerous and varied. Even at this day they repay study. Let us refresh our memories:

The principal form of Saluting As It Shouldn't is—

The Salute Selective

The most common example of this is for a bloke only to salute blokes in his own service. An airman, for instance, will stooge along, favouring the light blue and ignoring the dark blue almost as though he were up from Cambridge for Boat Race Day, and, as for the "brown jobs," he's apparently never heard of them. Or a sailor will salute a Sub-Lieutenant, though the latter is walking with a Wing-Commander—which, of course, makes for confusion. For both will acknowledge it, the latter because he's the senior and the former because he knows it's meant for him. The matlow thus gets two salutes and they have to chase after him and make him give one back.

Or again a private will dish out a cracking fine salute to a subaltern and completely ignore an Admiral just behind. This, of course, is highly embarrassing for the subaltern, should he turn round and see that he's apparently acknowledged a salute due to a senior officer of the senior service. Thereafter he walks in fear and dread, and, having once turned round, walks on and turns no more his head, because he knows a you-know-what doth close behind him tread. (After you, Claude? No, after *you*, Coleridge.) It's also embarrassing for the Admiral, if he acknowledges the salute as his natural due, for the private is apt to fix him with a hostile stare amounting almost to an open accusation of theft.

Another development of selective saluting is to pick your salutees by merit. You are, of course, the chap who decides the particular form of merit. I believe the W.A.A.Fs. started this. Not having to salute officers of the R.A.F. except as a matter of courtesy, some of them got into the rather generous habit of saluting those officers they particularly liked the look of—for, of course, various feminine reasons. Some saluted those who resembled favourite film stars; others those who had nice eyes, or who just seeemd so lonely, and so on—you know what women are—and the idea caught on among the troops. I don't mean an Australian private will only salute those officers who seem so lonely or have nice eyes, but you will find last war veterans who will pass aloofly and even contemptuously by young unmedalled Group-Captains with their caps simply smothered in scrambled egg, and then salute the Mons ribbon on some old dug-out Lieutenant's breast.

We'll now move to the other forms of Saluting As It Shouldn't.

The Salute Ignorant

This, of course, is given by those who don't know any better to those who look what they aren't. Thus, a Coldstream Guards subaltern—who wears gold round the peak of his cap—is frequently taken by new and innocent infantry subalterns for some sort of rather junior General and gets obsequiously saluted—and often acknowledges it. Whether, however, he acknowledges it in order not to embarrass an equal in rank, or whether he acknowledges it as his due from lower forms of Army life, such as the P.B.I., is rather moot.

The presence of foreign armies also increases the number of Salutes Ignorant. The Americans, for instance, are most difficult. When a young American Brigadier, who wears one single star (in England the Second Lieutenant's badge), passes an elderly British Captain, wearing three stars (in America a Lieutenant-General), it's very difficult to know who thinks he's saluting whom or acknowledging what, especially when both say "Good morning, sir." There was a suggestion at the time that some sort of simple Inter-Oceanic greeting was required, such as "Hiya, mate—wotcheer, buddie!" But it came to nothing.

Of course the best of the Salutes Ignorant are those received by the Commissionaires outside famous London hotels, who are always being mistaken for Free Azerbaijanian Generals or the like. It's one of the ironies of life, by the way, that when you salute a Commissionaire he ignores you contemptuously, but at the times when *he* salutes *you*, you can't ignore him: it costs sixpence or a shilling, depending on whether he's only held open a door or called the cab as well.

Once a Salute Ignorant has been made and realised as an error, it is difficult to get out of. It needs quick thinking, such as hurriedly putting the hand up to the cap again, removing the cap and brushing an imaginary spider off the peak, as if that's what you were really aiming to do all along. Don't overdo this, however; people in the Services who deal in

F

imaginary spiders are rather frowned on as having doubtful war-effort value. A quick tongue sometimes helps, such as explaining with a friendly smile, "Touch of my old rheumatism," and then continuing to bend and flex the arm in a series of actions gradually less and less like a salute.

Beware of having too quick a tongue, though. I knew a subaltern who once inadvertently saluted a very, very elderly captain with medals almost back to Omdurman, standing motionless and lost in thought at a bus stop. The captain came to life and barked, "Don't you know a captain's not entitled to your salute?" The subaltern replied, "No, but a corpse is." This in a way got him out of it, but he had to endure a lot of blistering invective—mostly Hindustani, but Tamil and Arabic came into it. The subaltern always swore afterwards that all traffic lights in range simultaneously went to red and stayed that way for seven minutes.

The Salute Courteous

This is really almost Selective Saluting, because it seems to be given for some special reason of the saluter's. For instance, an infantry sergeant walking down a quiet street with his arm round a blonde popsy will suddenly straighten up, pop the dropsy—I mean leave go of the girl—and put on a big saluting act in the most amiable manner for a quite uninterested Flight-Lieutenant with the D.F.C. His reason is generally obscure. It may be he thinks highly of the D.F.C.: it may be the officer's face reminds him of someone: it may be he has recently cut out a member of the R.A.F. in the matter of the blonde popsy and is making vicarious amends: or it may be he just wants to do this good salute for the day.

Anyway, over it comes—the Salute Courteous. It expresses an enormous affability coupled with a sort of unspoken message of "here's-you-and-me-and-what-a-game-it-all-is-why-in-civvy-street-we'd-probably-be-having-a-drink-to-gether." It is frequently accompanied by a winning but quite unexpected grin. The whole thing has indeed an atmosphere of fleeting but effusive camaraderie, only met with at Old School Dinners. This atmosphere, however, is soon dispelled by the popsy's very visible fury at being abruptly unlimbered and abandoned and—if she happens to be on the wrong side of her escort—getting her hat tilted over her ear by his elbow.

The Salute Courteous often passes between impressionable young W.A.A.Fs. and good-looking officers. Sometimes, if the officer is impressionable too, the acknowledgment comes well before the salute. The girl can't do anything about this, of course, such as handing him a freezing glance or giving him in charge. That's practically discourteous to the King: and, what the hell—one's only young once. . . .

The Salute Obsequious

This is given by Sub-Lieutenants, Second-Lieutenants, and so on, to Vice-Admirals, Major-Generals and upwards, under whom they are serving. The general object of the exercise is to get yourself noticed, and to draw the attention of the salutee to the fact that you're a jolly fine type worthy of instant promotion; but there's no reason to suppose it ever works. Indeed, if the General or what not is carrying a heavy parcel for his wife in one hand, a heavy portfolio in the other and a heavy liver somewhere in between the two, it may even work the other way.

Moreover, since the salute is characterised by excessive up-snapping of arms, quivering of wrists, and looking frankly and fearlessly into the other fellow's eyes, it's as well not to overdo it, but to study your man. If he's a red-faced Colonel who looks as though he's had a bit of a thick night, sudden up-snappings of arms may break down his final vestige of control: while a quivering wrist may be the last straw in a world already quivering pretty considerably. Or if he's a permanently nervous type—as distinct from temporarily nervy —that frank, fearless gaze may only give him the impression that his tie is crooked and you're sneering at it. This doesn't help towards promotion—even less, if he puts a tentative hand up towards his tie and finds that in fact it *is* crooked.

The Salute Devastating

This may occur in several ways, but the following is a good example. A young and rather new soldier, laden with rifle, pack, haversack, gas-mask—in fact, the whole blooming Christmas Tree, plus kitbag—is drifting aimlessly about the burrows of the Underground trying to find the way to King's Cross—it always *is* King's Cross. Turning a corner, he suddenly meets a full-blown General.

Now, Generals have not so far entered into his brief military career to any great extent, but the iron of discipline has entered into his soul, and all that red and gold, he feels, is definitely Big Stuff. He recalls the admonitions of his not-so-distant recruit course ("Thumper! What did your sergeant say about meeting an officer?"), and realises a salute is very obviously indicated, particularly for such a Very Rare Officer as this. The suddenness of the encounter doesn't give the wretched lad time to realise further that salutes are not welcome in crowded Tubes. So he salutes— something after this way.

He drops his kit-bag—on the foot of a man following behind—and begins to salute with the right hand, at which point his rifle slung over his right shoulder slides on to his neck. This recalls to him that he mustn't salute with the hand when carrying a rifle, so he tried to unsling it with the laudable idea of sloping it and saluting with it—though even now an awful suspicion is crossing his mind that Generals really should have a "present arms." However, before he gets very far the rifle is thoroughly entangled with both his gas-mask and his haversack, and the piling swivel is hooked up in his left breast pocket. He hastily decides to give up the saluting-with-rifle idea and just get it slung on his left shoulder so that he can salute with his right hand.

Even this proves to be impracticable, for by now the rifle, intricately tied up with his clothing and equipment, is about as movable as a five-ton anchor wedged in a coral reef: while severe tugs seem only likely to disintegrate him altogether as a unit of the Forces. Moreover, the butt has hit a man next him on the elbow, who has several things to say about it: a crowd has piled up in front and behind: and the embarrassed General, in trying to escape the imminent carnage, has fallen over the kitbag. . . . Well, one needn't go on, but that's a fair specimen of the Salute Devastating. And all because a young recruit remembered—at the wrong time— what he'd been taught at his drill sergeant's knee.

The Salute Inescapable

For some reason, this is indulged in more frequently by the Navy than the other services. Maybe it's that brotherhood-of-the-seas feeling: but, anyway, it's generally a sailor and nearly always a first day on shore leave—with, as Kipling puts it, all that that implies. It goes something like this:

A matlow, obviously very happy, is tacking amiably along the pavement when he sees a naval officer approaching him. Now, a soldier or airman in similar circumstances would, if he had any sense, take avoiding action at this point by setting a course down a side street, but the sailor is having no truck with things like sense on his first day ashore. He decides to go through with it and salute this officer.

And after all, he tells himself as he considered the matter

more deeply, it's not a question of his *deciding* to salute. He damwell *has to* salute. This officer is an officer, and it's the regulations. Moreover, he's proud to salute any naval officer; all brothers under the skin, all sailors under the gold braid. . . .

At this point the officer, who has had a weather eye on the situation, decides tactfully to look in a shop window till the matlow has passed. The latter, however, having made up his mind he has to salute, is not going to be put off by subterfuge. And it's no longer now even a question of *having* to salute. Why, he *wants* to salute.

So he also stops and looks in a shop window till the other is ready to move on. It's a privilege to salute such a nice naval officer as this naval officer evidently is. Fine type! Born leader! Never served under a better! Not that he's ever served under him at all, but he's now got around to thinking that way. . . .

Catching sight of his reflection in the window, he is taken a little aback. Who is this sloppy-looking son of a sea-cook? Disgrace to the Service! That cap on the back of the head, that overblown quiff of hair. Can't salute an officer looking like that.

He immediately embarks on a hasty toilet to make himself fit for the impending ceremony, and on finishing looks up to see that the officer, finding the shop-window gambit ignored, has apparently changed his mind and is now walking off the other way. . . .

Here, this won't do at all, thinks the sailor. This officer is due for his salute, one of the very best salutes, and now he won't get it. He toys with the idea of calling him back to be saluted, luckily thinks better of it, and sets off in pursuit.

The officer, who has had experience of affable sailors on leave and doesn't want any trouble, rings down to the engine-room for a full head of steam and whips up several more knots. The sailor does the same—a trifle indignantly. He's decided to salute this officer: this officer is entitled to a salute: this officer has damwell got to *have* a salute.

So off they go down turnings, across roads, in shops one way and out another, the officer dodging and twisting—but the result is inevitable. Sooner or later he'll have to give in, turn and walk past his pursuer and get it over with. Slightly out of breath, but with an air of respectful triumph, the matlow will then salute him and with any luck won't be able to think of a few welcoming words to go with it before the other is out of earshot. If the officer had been more experienced, he would have gone through with it in the first place, for it's the Salute Inescapable and there's no dodging it—unless he takes a taxi.

And even then the sailor is quite capable of getting in at one door, saluting him and getting out at the other.

The Salute From Ambush

A Flight-Lieutenant, say, is walking along the Strand with his best girl. He is smoking, talking to her, carrying a parcel—or rather six recently-purchased pairs of socks folded in an innocent newspaper—and the girl has just asked him to hold her bag for a moment while she adjusts her hat.

At this point two R.A.F. Military Policemen lurking in a doorway spot what is going on. Target for to-night, they mutter, and go into action.

Now, Military Police being very punctilious in saluting etiquette—they darn well have to be!—this means that they suddenly click their heels like pistol shots and salute in a manner that would strike even Royalty as being slightly overdone. The wretched officer, thus assailed from ambush, tries to clear for action; for he has to get both hands empty, one to remove his cigarette and the other to acknowledge the salute. . . .

Well, the general effect, of course, is of a man shot through the heart, and for several minutes afterwards the pavement is littered with socks, newspapers, cigarettes, and all those things girls have in their bags. The Military Police ignore the whole situation. They just gaze blankly into space—waiting for the next victim.

The Salute Insubordinate

At first this seems a contradiction, but it isn't really. There are, in fact, several kinds of Salute Insubordinate. Here is one:

Second-Lieutenant Swordfrog, soon after joining the Battalion, sees fit to tell off Company-Sergeant-Major Magazine, one of those old-time C.S.Ms. with *yeeeeers* of experience behind him. When he finishes, faltering towards the end, for it dawns on him he is making a major social *gaffe*, Magazine says, "Very good, sir," in a controlled sort of voice which sounds rather like the casing of a hand-grenade, steps back a pace and salutes punctiliously and smartly.

It will, however, be a Salute Insubordinate: but Swordfrog can't put a finger on just why, for, as we said, C.S.M. Magazine has had *yeeeers* of experience. Nevertheless, the slightly exaggerated smartness, the offensive quiver of the hand, the glassy stare over Swordfrog's right shoulder, and the imperceptible movement of the lips constitute something that, tried on Lieutenant-Colonel Howitzer, would result in Magazine having to hew his way up from Corporal once more. He doesn't actually spit on the ground—but the impressionable Swordfrog almost looks to see if he has, and for the next week goes to incredible lengths to avoid meeting C.S.M. Magazine; or, if he does, he knowledges the salute so fulsomely that it might have been given by a lovely blonde A.T.S. After a while C.S.M. Magazine lets it drop and salutes normally. Another single-pipper has learned his lesson.

At the other end of the scale comes quite a different type

of Salute Insubordinate—and one which this time has its dangers for the saluter. Here's an example:

Sergeant-Pilot Flash-Alf has just gone straight from air-man to sergeant—and the promotion has gone equally straight to his head. He is a Knight of the Sky, an intrepid bird-man; he wears his flying-helmet and a four-foot scarf into the local; he has had his photo taken in full kit from a position apparently six inches above ground level. By way of cutting out all useless dead wood, he gives up saluting any of the unwinged groundlings, except when it is forced upon him, and then he gives a careless superior sort of flick that would be considered offensive even as an acknowledgment by General Wavell to a half-drunk private.

He tries this, however, once too often when he deals one out in Whitehall to Flight-Lieutenant Trenchrayde, who has no wings but several decorations gained in the infantry in the last war at a considerably closer range to the enemy than Flash-Alf is ever likely to be in his whole life. As Sergeant Flash-Alf passes on, Flight-Lieutenant Trenchrayde yells, "*Oi! You!*" in a voice which used to bring his men over the top like springs coming out of a broken-down sofa. Flash-Alf stops as though lassooed round the neck. "Cum*mere!*" bawls Trenchrayde. Flash Alf returns as if under hypnotic influence. "Don't-you-*know*-how-to-salute-an-officer? Weren't-you-ever-*taught*-to-salute? I-don't-give-a-damn-if-you-don't-salute-me-*at-all*, but-by-Judas-if-you-do-you're-going-to-do-it-*right*-and-not-like-a-ruddy-errand-boy-waving-to-a-housemaid. . . ."

Well, that's only the politely conversational opening of what the elderly Flight-Lieutenant has to say about saluting, a subject, however, he soon leaves in favour of a brief résumé of Flash-Alf's career, appearance and habits, followed by a few recommendations for his immediate future actions, most of which are physiologially stimulating, but physically impracticable.

Blushing and stammering, and with his once pleasantly heavy chevrons feeling they might now float off into thin air any minute, Sergeant Flash-Alf is at last allowed to retire. As far as an acknowledgment of his salute goes, he has had it.

The Salute as a Practical Joke

In a way, the less said about this the kinder to all, for it is usually given by those who should know better to those who don't know enough.

A common exponent of this salute is an airman with a warped sense of humour—and far too many of them have this—coupled to a keen eye for potential victims. Thus equipped he is generally able to mark down a salutee whom he thinks (a) isn't expecting it, or (b) isn't in a position to return it. He will then salute suddenly and punctiliously, and hope that his time and trouble haven't been wasted.

If he is an expert, they won't have been—particularly if the victim is both (a) and (b). For what new young subaltern, the dew still fresh on his single pips, stooging happily along with his girl's arm in his, is in the least prepared for the Air Commodore some paces in front of him to be ignored by one of his own Service, while he himself—a despised brown job —is the sudden recipient of a salute like a cross between a galvanic shock and an attack of St. Vitus? (I hope, by the way, you have come out on the far side of that sentence in better shape than I have? Rather tiring I found it. Don't you agree?) For the moment he can hardly believe it's meant for him, and glances quickly over his shoulder to see if Field-Marshal Montgomery is just behind. Actually he isn't; so the subaltern quickly attempts an efficient acknowledgment.

Naturally it is anything but efficient, because he has his girl's arm and his stick and his gloves to cope with, and they're all in the wrong places—a fact which, of course, the

airman has been counting upon. Yet he can't ignore this
tribute to his commission. So he does his best, hampered
as he is by women and other impedimenta.

It isn't a very good best. He knows this and at once
becomes exceedingly morose and unhappy about the whole
thing. He even thinks of resigning next day. He snaps back
at his girl, who has probably remarked tactlessly, "What a
smart airman that was, darling. Why aren't you in the
R.A.F.?" She tells him off in return: and when the next
unfortunate salutes him he takes it out with a vicious acknowledgment. He is just too late to realise that there is then a
Very Senior Officer just behind him, who proceeds to take
an almost tangibly poor view of the back of his neck for the
next twenty yards. . . . Well, in short the whole thing from
the original airman's point of view has been pretty successful.

Another form of the Salute as a Practical Joke is to salute
in peculiar places. A soldier, young in years, but old in guile,
will suddenly put on a stupid look, as though he weren't
certain of the regulations, but feels that it's better to give a
superfluous salute than to fail to salute at all. Wearing this
as protective armour, he will crack one out in a Tube lift at
an elderly naval captain carrying home the week's rations for
his wife and trying to look as though they were important
documents. Or at a Squadron-Leader standing next him in a
crowded bus—one who is a little too tall to stand in a bus
and certainly to do any saluting in it. Or at an officer just
about to mount his bicycle; a carefully-chosen officer, too,
that is to say an officer who has obviously only just taken
again to bicycling after twenty years.

Finally, an excellent way of achieving the Practical Joke
Salute is for the saluter to lie in wait outside a shop till an
officer comes out with one hand in his pocket and a pre-
occupied look. He is almost certain to be putting his change
back after a purchase and at the same time checking it to see
if it's right. A smart, forcing salute will probably, therefore,

bring his hand sharply out of his pocket to acknowledge it—so sharply that he won't be able to let go of his money in time. The result will be most gratifying—a shower of coinage, in all directions.

I find, by the way, I have omitted to record the very best example of the Salute as a Practical Joke. That is where the saluter raises his hand and arm smartly, as if to salute, and then merely adjusts his cap or scratches his head, or removes a fag from behind the right ear. With any luck, the officer will start to acknowledge and can then be stared at in a pained manner, while a genuine salute is given, as if the saluter took a pretty dim view of people who insist on the paying of unnecessary compliments in crowded streets. Of course, the officer himself may be about to adjust his cap, or scratch his head, or remove a fag from behind his ear—in which case the would-be joker has had it.

Remember that the Salute as a Practical Joke is inclined to be dangerous if the wrong victim is picked. Try it on a peppery, old-time Colonel, for example, and you'll soon realise there's really no future at all in it.

The Salute Unintentional

This is the kind of salute in which two people get involved without either of them in the least wanting to. Here is a very common example. A sprog P.O. and a just-joined erk—I should say, a newly-commissioned Pilot Officer and an Air Force recruit—are approaching one another in the Strand. The erk has already noticed that though the place is alive with officers, yet not much saluting is being pushed out, except for the higher grades. Old London custom, he's beginning to suppose. Being new, however, he's so far been conscientiously and automatically saluting everyone entitled to same, till his arm aches, and has now just got to the stage of feeling that he will at any rate let this very junior officer go by default.

Now the P.O. has also been conscientiously doing a lot of saluting and acknowledging of salutes, and being new, doing it with considerable fervour. *His* arm is also weary. *He* also is hoping that this approaching airman won't insist on formality.

Each, therefore, prepares studiously to ignore the other, to pass like ships in the night—well, not like ships in the night, because, now I come to think of it, they speak each other in passing—but like ships that pass in a very dark night, ten-tenths cloud and Visibility Nought, who don't know there's another ship in miles.

They are, however, both pretty self-conscious about it. The erk is darting surreptitious and apprehensive glances in various directions, in case any Red-cap is in the vicinity who may put him on the hooks for failing to salute an officer and at the same time in trying to look as if he didn't know there was an officer within a thousand yards of him. The P.O. is also trying to look as if he didn't know there was an airman within a thousand yards of him, and at the same time is darting surreptitious and apprehensive glances at him in case he salutes and he fails to acknowledge it—which, of course, would be a terrible *faux pas*. All in all, it's a tense moment.

Well, naturally it happens that just as they are almost abreast a surreptitious and apprehensive glance from the erk connected with a surreptitious and apprehensive glance from the officer. "Gawd," thinks the erk, "he means me to salute." "Gosh," thinks the P.O., "he means to salute me," and at once tries to put a stopper on it by looking away quickly—just as the erk, resigned now to going through with it, starts to salute. But seeing the officer look away, the latter realises he's misjudged the fellow and hastily turns his action into a check-up on whether his right breast-pocket button is correctly fastened. At the same moment, however, the P.O. has seen the start of the salute from the corner of his eye, and realises that this over-punctilious young airman is apparently quite determined to "pay the compliment." He, therefore, starts to acknowledge it.

This catches the wretched erk completely off balance. Not to see an officer is one thing, to look at him and then wilfully button up a pocket at him is another. He at once carries his pocket-buttoning move straight on into an awkward scrambled touching of the cap. By now, however, the P.O. has realised he was about to acknowledge a salute that wasn't there, which, of course, is an even worse *faux pas* than not acknowledging a salute that was. So he too turns his acknowledgment into a check-up on his breast-pocket button—only to find he is being saluted after all, though in rather a peculiar fashion. He at once changes his action into an equally peculiar acknowledgment.

Flushing deeply, trying to avoid each other's eyes and yet catching them by a sort of mesmeric compulsion, the two manage to get past one another, though their day is completely spoilt and they spend the rest of it saluting or acknowledging the salutes of every figure in uniform who so much as glances in their direction.

And that is the Salute Unintentional. How much better would it not have been to have waved happily, called out, "Hiya, toots" or something, and passed on into a world better and brighter for the encounter?

The Salute Quite Incredible

Doubtless many forms of this are known to readers, but it only happened once in my experience. After all, it is the kind of salute that *can* only happen once in any one person's lifetime. The one I saw went like this:

A young infantry Captain had just come out of a tobacconist's with a box of cigarettes in his right hand and his stick and gloves in the other, when he encountered a private passing the adjoining shop, which was a butcher's. The private was on leave and taking his dog for a walk. . . . I should perhaps here point out that the Salute Quite Incredible demands a certain amount of stage-setting and props, but that's only to be expected. After all you can't put on, say, a play like *The Ghost Train* successfully in the back drawing-room with a cast from the local Kindergarten.

Well, the private took the dog-lead in the left hand and started to salute. The captain shoved the cigarettes hastily in his mackintosh pocket and prepared to acknowledge it. So far, all buttoned up and under control.

Unfortunately the private, in bringing his arm smartly up, hit his elbow an almighty whop on one of those long poles with a hook that hang on an iron rail outside butchers' shops and are used to garner in the more retiring joints from up in the back rows of the gallery.

The sudden noise of the impact—to say nothing of a virulent oath which does not usually accompany salutes— startled the officer so much that, missing his mackintosh pocket he put the cigarettes instead right through the slit thoughtfully made to allow direct access from outside to the tunic pocket. This, of course, meant that they went straight down inside his mackintosh on to the pavement.

The private, by then at the salute, had to cut it off short to check the dog who thought the officer wanted a game of retrieving. Bending down to restrain him, he was just in time to sustain a nasty attack in the base area from the pole, which, having swung away at the impact of his elbow, had now swung joyfully back into the fray.

This precipitated him forward into the captain, also bending down to grab his cigarettes before the dog did. Their heads met with a crack: the officer lost his stick and gloves, and the private his cap.

The captain, concentrating on essentials, picked up the cigarettes. The much-flustered private picked up his cap, one glove and the stick, gave the stick and cap to the captain and momentarily tried to put the glove on his head. The dog, having lost the cigarettes, picked up the other glove and started off down the street. He didn't get far, because he'd by then got his lead round his master's leg. This brought him up all standing and the private all sitting. The butcher came out and said, "What are you two playing at? . . ."

Well, I didn't wait to see any more, feeling that no one would ever believe what had happened so far. But it was a perfect example of the Salute Quite Incredible. The only other I have heard of which might be called this type was just an ordinary military salute. But it was given to a British Staff Officer by an Australian private. True, the Australian did first look round furtively in case any of his friends were watching him. The Staff Officer, of course, fainted. . . .

Printed in Great Britain by
The Camelot Press Ltd., London and Southampton